# Andreas Spreinat

# Lake Malawi Cichlids from Tanzania

*Pseudotropheus* "Tropheops Mutant", photographed at Cove Mountain.

# Andreas Spreinat

# Lake Malawi Cichlids
# from Tanzania

Photos by the author unless otherwise mentioned

Cover photo: *Pseudotropheus* "Zebra Gold Breast Orange Top" at Hongi Island.

ISBN 3-931328-00-7

© 1995 Dr. Andreas Spreinat
Unterm Hagen 4, D-37079 Göttingen
Printed in Germany

Marketing/Distribution: Verduijn Cichlids • Wollefoppenweg 107
        NL-2761 DL Zevenhuizen • Tel. +31-104550253 • Fax +31-104566738

Translation: Regine Fadiman • Ann Arbor • Michigan • USA
Typesetting & Coverdesign: Angela Meißner • Feldtorstraße 29 • D-37176 Nörten-Hardenberg
Illustrations: Andrea Knaust • Breite Straße 13 • D-37077 Göttingen
Lithos & Print: Bernecker Mediengruppe • Unter dem Schöneberg 1 • D-34212 Melsungen
Published by: A. Spreinat • Unterm Hagen 4 • D-37079 Göttingen

# Table of Contents

Rocky littoral at Nkanda.

Western shore of Ngkuyo Island: especially around the islands is the water visibility very good.

# Foreword

Since the early 1960s, when the first live cichlids from Lake Malawi were introduced to Europe and the United States, interest in these fish has been increasing steadily. This interest is by no means limited to aquarists who raise and breed these colorful mouthbrooders, as many scientists in the 1970s and 1980s carried out extensive investigations on the ecology and taxonomy of this fish group, which is unique in the entire world.

Remarkably enough, nearly all data on Lake Malawi cichlids were collected on the coast of Malawi. As for species from the other two border states, namely Tanzania and Mozambique, hardly any scientific information exists.

In October and November 1993, I had the opportunity to explore the entire coastline of this lake in Tanzania by boat and to conduct underwater observations at several locations. The goal of the trip was to obtain a first overview of the cichlid fauna of this still largely unexplored area. Special emphasis was placed on the realistic reproduction of newly discovered species by means of underwater photography. The recent past has shown that clear morphological differences hardly exist between many of these species, which are comparatively young in evolutionary terms. However, most of the species can be identified with relative ease based solely on the typical coloration of the males and on their melanin pattern. The results of this five-week research trip essentially form the contents of this book.

My special thanks go to Erling Johansen and Laif DeMason, Lake Nyassa African Fishes Ltd. in Mbeya/Kyela, Tanzania, for support and liason work "on the spot". Without their help this book could not have been written. I would also like to express my thanks and appreciation to the members of their "crew" who accompanied me, especially my co-diver Mattayo Jackson, who on some days spent more time with me below water than above, as well as Friedrich "Freddy" Wolf, who during the week-long safaris that lasted for weeks, supplied us with gasoline and groceries, sometimes by outlandish means, thus enabling us to concentrate fully on our primary aims.

I also wish to thank all the people in Germany who made fish available for photographing, in particular, Markus Schlangen; Malawi-Tanganjika-Aquarium Neuß, Reinhold Müller; Frankfurt, as well as Mark Danhieux and Thomas Lepel; Maltavi Hohenahr-Erda. My thanks also go to these individuals as well as to Lothar Seegers, Dinslaken, for many helpful discussions.

Last but not least, I would like to mention that none of my cichlidophile activities could have been carried out without the support and active cooperation of my wife Kerstin; in the end my deepest thanks and sincere admiration go to her for she has not yet tired of her husband nor his hobby.

Göttingen, September 1994
Andreas Spreinat

Group of *Pseudotropheus* "Daktari" at Hai Reef.

# Introduction

With a north-south length of nearly 600 km and a maximal width of about 80 km, Lake Malawi is the third largest lake in Africa. It reaches a maximum depth of more than 700 m and its surface area is almost 31 000 sq. km. (FRYER & ILES 1972).

Among the many fascinating aspects of this lake, its most special feature is its fish fauna. Both in terms of overall numbers and in terms of the number of species, the largest fish family is undoubtedly represented by the cichlids. All other fish families occur in much smaller numbers. More than 400 cichlid species from Lake Malawi have been discovered to date. Nearly all of these species are endemic to Lake Malawi, i.e., they live only in this particular body of water and nowhere else on this planet. Interestingly enough, nearly all species are maternal mouthbrooders. Evolution biologists operate on the assumption that all endemic cichlid species in Lake Malawi have evolved from only one basic lineage (MEYER et al. 1990).

Three countries border on Lake Malawi: Malawi in the southeast and west, Tanzania in the northeast, and Mozambique centered on the eastern coast. Malawi has about 800 km of coastline. The coastline of Tanzania is roughly 300 km, and that of Mozambique about 200 km. The two largest islands in the lake, Likoma and Chisumulu, belong to Malawi.

Until its national independence (Malawi, or rather Nyasaland, was under British rule until 1964), this southern-most lake of the Great Rift Valley of East Africa was better known as Lake Nyasa (or Lake Nyassa). In the language of the Yao, Nyasa simply means "large water". The renaming of Lake Nyasa came in the wake of the political emancipation of Malawi from co-lonial rule. In Tanzania and Mozambique the name Lake Nyasa continues to be in use. Against this background, it would be logical to refer to the cichlids of the Tanzanian coastline as Lake Nyasa cichlids. However, in the following we decided to retain the term Lake Malawi cichlids so as to avoid semantic confusion. This is bound to happen as one compares species found in Tanzania with similar cichlids from Malawi, or if one speaks of general characteristics of these cichlids.

Ichthyological research on Lake Malawi started as early as the middle of the last century (GÜNTHER 1864) and was limited — with a few exceptions — to the coastal areas of Lake Malawi. We will briefly mention the most important studies.

## Malawi

At the beginning of this century, 38 species were included in the list of Lake Malawi cichlids (BOULENGER 1915). These species were collected in the course of several research trips and were described primarily by GÜNTHER (1864, 1893) and by BOULENGER (1908). More comprehensive research that was particularly important from a taxonomic viewpoint was carried out in the British Museum (Natural History) and presented in 1922 by REGAN, who at his time, counted 84 species. His student, the recently deceased Grand Dame of cichlid lore, Ethelwynn TREWAVAS, continued Regan's work and in 1931 published a revision of the genus *Lethrinops* (TREWAVAS 1931). Four years later, her much quoted "Survey" (synopsis) appeared on the cichlids of Lake Nyasa (TREWAVAS 1935). As a foundation, TREWAVAS used the large collection containing about 3500 preserved specimens that had been compiled by CHRISTY between 1925 and 1926 on a special expedition. In the synopsis, the number of species increased to 175, with a total of 23.

The 1950s saw the first publications on the ecology of cichlids of Lake Malawi (FRYER 1956b, 1959). ILES investigated the group of cichlids favoring more open water, today's *Copadichromis* spp. (ILES 1960). The works of these two authors led in 1972 to the publication of a comprehensive standard volume on the biology and evolution of cichlids of the Great Lakes of Africa (FRYER & ILES 1972). At the beginning of the 1960s, the first live Lake Malawi cichlids were exported, arousing the enthusiasm of aquarists everywhere. The 1970s and 1980s were characterized by much activity involving these vibrantly colorful species from a scientific as well as an aquaristic viewpoint. During this period, aquarists conducted their first journeys to this lake and discovered new species.

One of the first travel reports was published by STOLZ in 1972. Commercial exporters discovered and shipped numerous new species to every continent. A great many scientific and aquaristic reports were published. Among the groundbreaking publications of more recent times we will mention only two. One is the "Preliminary Survey" on Mbunas by RIBBINK and coworkers that appeared in 1983 and which represents the first comprehensive survey on Mbunas and is essentially a report of underwater observations (RIBBINK et al. 1983). An equally solid foundation is provided by the revision of the earlier "Haplochromis" species, presented by ECCLES and TREWAVAS in 1989, which divides that genus into several new genera (ECCLES & TREWAVAS 1989).

**Tanzania**

As detailed and diverse the knowledge may be of the cichlids of the coast of Malawi, very little is known of the northeastern coast, i.e., the coast of modern Tanzania. The first person to report on this area was AHL, who in 1927 initially published a description of several species. The type specimens had been collected by FÜLLEBORN in what was then German East Africa, namely at (Alt-)Langenburg (modern Lumbira). One of the best-known Lake Malawi cichlids was described by AHL, who named it after its discoverer, *Labeotropheus fuelleborni*. Other species, also well known to aquarists, are *Pseudotropheus macrophthalmus* and *Dimidiochromis kiwinge* (AHL 1927). FRYER, whose investigations were limited primarily to the coast of Malawi, in 1956 described *P. elongatus*, based on three specimens that he had caught in Mbamba Bay (FRYER 1956a). Although the name of this species is well known to most aquarists, and although in the past many species or forms have been traded under this name, the "genuine" *P. elongatus* has probably not been imported yet (cf. the discussion on the *P. elongatus* species-group).

It took a further 50 years after AHL before more research was conducted. W. STAECK traveled around the coastal region near the Livingstone Mountains and published the first photographs of several species (STAECK 1976). At the end of the 1980s and the beginning of the 1990s, more collection trips followed, organized on a private basis, and the first live specimens were exported to Germany (SEEGERS & KILIAN 1987, pers. comm.; SEEGERS 1991, 1992). Commercial activities by exporters of ornamental fish started around 1990/91. This considerably extended the logistical basis for future travel, as one of the main difficulties in these touristically completely unexplored regions is the organization of boats, fuel and other necessary equipment. Reports by aquarists on several new populations, observed in their natural habitat, have been published recently

(KNABE 1992, RUSS 1993, BENTLER 1993, DE-MASON 1993a, DeMASON 1994a, KONINGS 1994, LEPEL 1994). A first survey on the species exported to Germany was published in 1993 (SPREINAT 1993a, LEPEL 1993a).

The first investigations showed, as had been expected, that several species whose habitat is on the northwest coast also live on the Tanzanian coast. This is especially true of many Non-Mbunas, which are often distributed over the entire lake and are not just limited to certain coastal regions. Among the more rock-oriented Mbunas there are nevertheless some populations that occur on both the northeastern and northwestern coasts. However, most of these Mbunas belong to either new species, or subspecies and/or geographical races.

The following report is essentially based on the results of a five-week research trip carried out in October and November of 1993. We traveled the entire coast of Tanzania, from Ikombe on the northern tip to Hai Reef on the border of Mozambique in the south. The crew included Mattayo Jackson and, on a temporary basis, several staff members of the ornamental fish export firm Johansen and DeMason, LANYAFI Mbeya; this firm also supplied the boat for the trip. In the following, whenever the word "we" is used in connection with underwater observations, the plural includes Mattayo Jackson, who, as the diving partner of the author, spent countless hours under water with him.

Our excursion was divided into two parts. During the first trip, we traveled the northern coastal area from Ikombe to Lupingu (from north to south) and back. The second trip included the southern coastal areas, where we dived, starting from Mbamba Bay, proceeding in a southernly direction (Undu Point, Hai Reef), and then continued in a northernly direction to Magunga. During these trips we divided the coast into small manageable sections. In selected bays we set up camp (in Mbamba Bay guest houses were available for overnight stays) and proceeded to dive in the coastal areas north and south of our camp. After that, we would break camp and continue to the next camping place. In this way we hoped to obtain — as much as possible — a comprehensive survey of the various cichlid populations.

In order to study the natural habitats and to take underwater photographs, we almost exclusively used scuba diving gear, which, when necessary, could be refilled, using portable air compressors. For safety reasons, we limited maximum diving depth to about 50 meters. When diving, we primarily explored rocky or intermediate (mixed sand and stone/rock) habitats. We also made numerous observations in the adjacent sandy areas, but we did not dive over the large purely sandy areas which are frequently found off the southern coast of Tanzania. Some of the underwater photographs were taken during snorkeling expeditions in shallow water up to 5 meters deep, i.e., when we were armed with nothing more than goggles, snorkel and fins. This procedure, while very strenuous, turned out to be very successful for some cichlids. Many cichlids are highly sensitive to the loud noise of the breathing regulator and keep such a large distance from the diver that it is almost impossible to take good photographs. This is true in particular for many *Nyassachromis* and *Lethrinops* spp., among which even the territorial males, which in other species take little notice of the presence of divers, immediately react with flight behavior.

Observations in natural habitats are, of course, more successful if one can directly compare several species with each other in the same area. In order also to be able to compare populations later on, and also to facilitate comparison with Malawian populations, we tried not to concentrate on the most brilliantly colored males when photographing, but also to photograph the relatively inconspicuous or otherwise unusual specimens. With respect to this, it should be pointed out that in the past little attention has been paid to variation in either patterns or color characteristics within a species. Some species vary not only from one location to another (local forms), but also even at the same location one can sometimes find quite differently colored examples of the same species. Taking this factor into consideration, more than 2700 underwater photographs were produced and analyzed from the viewpoints outlined above.

We were able to catch a great number of species with nets while we were diving, enabling us to examine, for example, their teeth when in doubt about their identity. Another way of obtaining data on distribution of different species is by simply looking at the catch of local fishermen. As a diver, one rarely gets to see some of the species that live in purely sandy regions, in murky river estuaries or in open water; thus the local catch can be very enlightening indeed.

In conclusion, it should be noted that during our expedition we found a number of new species, revised the definition of distribution areas of species already known and generally obtained new data. All things considered, however, a five-week research trip cannot provide a comprehensive survey. Further discoveries on these coasts are sure to come. Many recent studies that have been carried out in Malawi have shown that particularly from a taxonomic viewpoint it is very difficult to present conclusive results. This is all the more remarkable since in these waters research has been carried out for decades. Against this background, this book is presented as a primary foundation and orientation aid for subsequent work on the cichlids of the Tanzanian coast.

# Notes on the use of this book

In the preceding chapter we briefly explained how the following investigations were carried out and how the findings presented here were obtained. In addition, some general remarks seem appropriate for better understanding. Explanations concerning the use of different cichlid names are covered in their own section (see below), so that few comments on that subject need to be repeated here.

## Name

Scientific names are not explained, since a reference is made to the author who first described a particular species scientifically. As for trade or working names (names that are capitalized and in quotation marks), the origin of the name is given and its meaning, if known, is explained. Trade names were adopted if the species in question has already been mentioned in the literature under this name or if the trade name is well known in aquaristic circles. If a species has been known in the literature under several trade names, the older name was selected, unless the younger name had found broad acceptance among aquarists while the older name — for whatever reasons — remained unknown.

(Example: *Labidochromis* "Hongi" has been bred frequently in captivity and is well known to aquarists. Various reports about this cichlid use the expression "Hongi" which refers to the island of the same name. However, this species was first mentioned as *L.* "Puulu" in the literature.)

As for commercial names, it must be kept in mind that cichlids from the northeastern coast have been traded since the beginning of the 1990s by at least three different exporters. New wild-caught species are commonly given trade or working names by catchers or exporters. Consequently, it may happen that one species is traded in aquaristic circles under three different names. When naming those species which had been observed by us but still had not been described scientifically, we had to be careful about not creating unnecessary confusion in cases involving species that had already been imported.

## Characteristics

The category "Characteristics" that appears in the descriptions of the individual species has on one hand been limited to a few essential elements that might possibly not be recognized from the color photographs. On the other hand, we wanted to draw the reader's attention to certain peculiarities, which on the whole, are not immediately apparent to the inexperienced cichlidophile. Particularly in need of explanation are the data on size, which always refer to total length (i.e., including the caudal fin). Many Mbunas vary considerably with respect to size and relative depth of body according to food availability. This effect can be demonstrated at some points in the lake itself, but it becomes especially apparent in an aquarium. If food is abundant, the Mbunas, accustomed to Aufwuchs, which is rich in ballast and hence relatively poor in nutrition, grow markedly bigger than under natural conditions. Thus the members of the genus *Labidochromis*, normally relatively small at a length of 7 to 8 cm, easily reach lengths of 10 or 12 cm and become high-backed or massive in the process. This also applies to a lesser degree to representatives of the genus *Aulonocara* and other Non-Mbunas. The total lengths quoted refer to the specimens that we found in their natural biotope, and hence are to be understood as reference values. Further-more, we could not catch every species and an estimate of size was obtained by comparison with other species of the same biotope, the size of which was known.

## Distribution

The data presented here, apart from our own observations, of course also take into consideration already known and reliably verified locations of the cichlid species in question. The latter information will either be put in quotation marks or we will refer to the source of information in question. In the case of some Mbunas, a species was encountered in many places, all of which were connected by rocky coastal regions. Hence, it must not be assumed that "gaps" exist in the distribution area between locations (as they so often do for these rock-frequenting species in the form of sandy beaches or river estuaries). Nevertheless, in these cases we did not dispense with the citation of the places of discovery. Another reason for this is that in some cases we tried in vain to find a species in specific areas, even though the species in question occurred frequently in the adjacent coastal areas to the north and south, and even though to all appearances, the biotopes were not basically different. Despite these rather special problematic situations, it should be expected that future investigations will uncover further locations for many of the species introduced in the following pages. History has shown that in the past distribution areas of Mbunas were generally underestimated in terms of size.

## Habitat and feeding

For the data on habitat similar restrictions apply as in the case of distribution areas. Most species prefer certain substrata or depths. As an aside, I would like to mention that several species, albeit in much smaller numbers, occasionally will be sighted in untypical biotopes. The habitat preferences of a certain species often not only apply to certain depths or the general type of substratum, but also to small-scale structures of a biotope, as represented, for example, by small to medium-sized stones or large rocks. In this connection, we used the following rough classification: stones of ca 5 to 20 cm in diameter — small stones; 20 to 50 cm — medium-sized stones; up to 1 m — large stones; more than 1 m — rocks. The expression "large rocks" refers to rocks of at least several cubic meters. The terms "mixed substrate" or "intermediate habitats" (FRYER 1959) are generally used to describe areas in which free sandy areas alternate with stones or rocks. Many sections of coast contain such mixed bottoms. In deep water of ca 40 meters, most rocky or stony areas usually change into sandy or muddy bottom and thus form intermediate habitats in transition. Since all kinds of other transition varieties may occur, the above classification should be understood as a rough guide only, which does not diminish its usefulness.

Data on depth must generally be considered with caution. Granted, it is relatively simple to determine the depth distribution of a cichlid species at a certain location. One dives into the depth profile and estimates how many individuals occur at a given depth per area. Here, one must keep in mind that to a certain extent depth distribution is strongly influenced by the quality of the habitat. Thus it appears to be irrelevant for many species whether they live at depths of 5 or 25 m, as long as suitable hiding places exist and, of course, food. The latter fact is especially crucial for Mbunas feeding on rock-associated Aufwuchs. Algal growth, which is the basis for the abundant occurrence of microorganisms in the algal mat, depends of course on sunlight. The deeper the water, the less sun energy is available for algae. In our diving excursions we got the impression that shallow water favors the especially strong and assertive or even aggressive species, while other, weaker species are expelled to the deeper and nutritionally poorer areas. This inter-specific competition could also be the reason that one may find a certain species in the same habitat at one location in shallow water, but at another only at depths of 20 m or more.

Data on feeding habits originate exclusively from underwater observations.

## Similar species

In this category, species are listed that are similar with respect to the criteria of body shape, shape of mouth, melanin pattern and coloration. We emphasize that such similarities frequently, but not necessarily, are indicators for close relationships. The holistic observation of species with respect to species-specific variation is very helpful when one is concerned with recognizing and drawing distinctions between different species. Particularly for Mbunas, the purely morphological approach is not very meaningful because of the lack of clear criteria or species-specific features. For the analysis of forms and coloration it is, however, important to "get the hang of" observing, so as to be able to make proper classifications. The classification of Lake Malawi cichlids among themselves, i.e., the definition of meaningful criteria for the determination of relationships, remains one of the most complex and difficult tasks (cf. RIBBINK et al. 1983: 153–155).

In principle, all data not otherwise designated are based on our own observations. To avoid improper generalizations, in those cases where only few observations existed, we chose formulations like "we only encountered this cichlid in deep water" and not statements like "this cichlid lives in deep water".

# Cichlid names and taxonomy

In the context of Lake Malawi cichlids there have been complaints in aquaristic circles about a "Babylonian confusion of language" since 1973 (ZIERZ 1973). Nothing has improved in this state of affairs; if anything, the opposite has taken place. The reasons for this can only be explained in passing.

To obtain a scientifically valid name, the cichlid in question must be examined and it must be shown that it is not identical to another, already described species. The results must be published under certain criteria in such a way that they are accessible to everyone. In this "first description" the species is assigned to a certain genus (or an entirely new genus may be described) and a latinized species name is conferred. Furthermore, the type specimens should be deposited at a museum so that, if necessary, subsequent investigations can be carried out, for example, if the author of the first description has erred, and no new species is involved at all. Among the type specimens a holotype should be determined, which is the only relevant specimen for the species in question. All other type specimens are called paratypes. This procedure has the advantage that there is no confusion about which specimen is the standard one, should it turn out later that the type specimens belong to different species.

The identification of a species is therefore connected with the question of whether it concerns a new or an already described species. Unfortunately, many of the old first descriptions are based exclusively on preserved specimens; often neither the location of discovery nor the live coloration are known, and merely morphological and morphometric data have been collected. This means that it might be very difficult to answer the question of identification. A precise investigation of the type material or a precise comparison of already described species with the newly-caught cichlids is often indispensable. The amount of work connected with this cannot possibly be carried out by an exporter or importer of ornamental fish. Consequently, there are three possible scenarios. First, the species involved is easy to recognize and is correctly classified within an already described species. Second, the species involved is incorrectly classified, i.e., offered in trade, for example, incorrectly as *Pseudotropheus elongatus*. As soon as the right, "genuine" *P. elongatus* is caught or it is otherwise determined that this is not the right species, the cichlid in question must again be subjected to the question of identification. At any rate, a new name has to be found, which means re-education. Third, the cichlid involved cannot be classified within any species. If this is the case, the new species would be described and would so receive a scientific name.

Since a first description also involves a great amount of work —which may take several months and can only be carried out by expert and experienced persons — another path is often chosen. The new species receives a "tentative" working or trade name that characterizes the species in question, thus giving subsequent researchers a chance to establish a point of reference.

For example, all the species discovered by RIBBINK et al. during their years of research in Malawi were not described scientifically, but had working names bestowed on them (RIBBINK et al. 1983).

Scientific names are written in *italics* (*Pseudotropheus elongatus*). Working names (trade names) are set within quotation marks. It goes without saying that one should not use latinized working names. To make the distinction vis-à-vis scientific names even clearer, working names are capitalized (*Pseudotropheus* "Broad Bar"). Some authors also use the addition "species", "spec." or even shorter, "sp." (*Pseudotropheus* spec. "Broad Bar"). However, this is unnecessary and considerably upsets the alphabetical order. The same goes for another method of naming undescribed species, where the species name precedes the genus name instead of following it, and where in addition the genus name has been anglicized and thus is no longer written in Italics (Broad Bar Pseudotropheus). For ease of comprehension, it is, in principle, desirable to bestow working names which emphasize specific features of the cichlid in question. This may be the location of discovery or an important characteristic. One must keep in mind, of course, that it may turn out later that the choice of working name was not a happy one. For example, if a species has been named after the location of discovery, it could happen that later on this same cichlid is found much more frequently at other locations in the lake and the first population represents merely a marginal population. If a certain color feature is included in the name, it might turn out that the new species is very variable in this respect and that other populations do not exhibit this particular feature at all. In any case, however, it is absolutely necessary to retain the original working name. Otherwise the semantic confusion mentioned above would only be further increased.

Other factors that have contributed to the confusion are primarily the renaming of species, the invention of new names although working names existed and the incorrect transmission of names. The bestowing of working names that contain personal names or represent pure fantasy creations are also not a good idea. A fitting example in this context is *Pseudotropheus* "Kingsize" from the island of Likoma. This cichlid is by no means — as the trade name would lead one to believe — particularly large. Rather, at an overall length of 8 to 10 cm this cichlid is among the smaller Mbunas. The trade name represents the latinized given name of the native catcher Kingsize Mchanda, who presumably was the first to catch this species. The appellation was created by a fish exporter.

The working names conferred in the following text were selected according to the above criteria. English working names were used for pragmatic reasons only. The past has shown that many English-speaking aquarists have difficulties with German working names, while in the reverse case the necessary language skills exist, so there are no problems concerning the handling of English expressions.

In conclusion, some comments on the peculiarities of the different names are given.

The addition "cf." (*Pseudotropheus* cf. *williamsi*, from the Latin conferre = to compare) before the species name indicates that this might be the species in question, but that the author is not entirely sure about it. This addendum should only be used if there are clear indications for concluding that this might be the species in question. In contrast, the addendum "aff." (from the Latin affinis = related) is used if a related, but not the same species, is concerned. This form of name expansion used to be common, but has been dropped recently. The reason is that there are many closely related, undescribed species, thus this addendum has little informative value.

Numerous *Pseudotropheus* species are summarized in so-called species-groups and species-complexes (RIBBINK et al. 1983). Thus, all elongate species that resemble *Pseudotropheus elongatus* are classified as *P. elongatus* species-group. In order to include this in working names, the actual working name is given by the addendum "Elongatus" (e.g., *P.* "Elongatus Luhuchi").

For species that live along various coastal regions and have evolved different color forms (local forms), it makes sense to include the location of discovery in parentheses (*Pseudotropheus* "Msobo" (Magunga)). If in contrast the location of discovery is mentioned in the working name, the author in question assumes that an independent species is involved (e.g., *Pseudotropheus* "Tropheops Chilumba" and *Pseudotropheus* "Tropheops Mbamba"). Exceptions to these general conventions are noted in the text.

*Oreochromis* sp. in shallow water at Lupingu.

# Places and maps

Despite intensive efforts it was impossible (with a few exceptions) to obtain detailed maps of the northeastern shoreline of the lake. Accordingly, only the two survey maps of the entire lake and the northern part of the lake are drawn to scale, but not the two subsequent maps which reproduce individual coastal sections.

During our trips, in order to determine the relative position of the small villages, we approximately calculated their distances to the large settlements that were given in the survey maps. Here we based our calculations on the time required to travel by boat from one village to the next. On the basis of the time that we needed for known distances, we then computed the average speed of the boat. Naturally, this kind of procedure can only yield approximate data, since wind, current and swell all influence the speed of the boat. Many distances were traveled and measured twice (to and from the destination) and the deviations were not that large; therefore, our home-made maps must be relatively accurate.

Greater inaccuracies are likely to have occurred in our sketches of the shoreline of the individual sections. Here we had to rely on the naked eye and other rough estimates.

African place names, depending on the source, are often reproduced quite differently. In principle, this is not due to the fact that, for instance, different names are used for the same river, as happened in the history of Europe for political reasons or when the borders of countries shifted. Rather the names sound very similar, but are spelled differently. The largest river, which enters the lake along the northeastern coast south of Manda, is called Ruhuru. Other spellings are Ruhulu, Luhuru, or Luhulu. The different spellings in this case pertain to the letters R and L, which in some tribal languages are evidently not distinguished (Lumbira = Lumbila; Jaro Reef = Jalo Reef). A similar situation sometimes applies to the letters M and N (Mkiri = Nkiri = Nkili).

On English-language maps some place names along Malawi's coast have accordingly been transformed. Thus the original name for a small island in front of Chilumba (northwest coast) is Chitendi, which became Chitande in English. Often these deviations involve only the last letter (Mbenji Island = Mbenje Island).

In the case of islands or rock formations not known to us we asked native fishermen and let them spell the names for us. Examples are Mbahwa Island, a small island south of Hongi Island, or Luhuchi Rocks and Maunyuni Rocks at Mbamba Bay.

Two diving locations were named by us. "Cove Mountain" is located along the rocky coast north of Manda. The name refers to a mountain featuring a distinct, cove-like indentation which for that reason could hardly be overlooked. Along the shore directly at the foot of this mountain, we found high cichlid population densities.

The term "pontoon" refers to the pontoon that was sunk in Mbamba Bay, directly on the beach in shallow water opposite the rest house. Some of the steel cables that used to anchor the pontoon can still be seen from the beach.

In the following table all places and coastal sections at which we carried out diving excursions are summarized. If only the place name is given, the underwater observations refer to the coastal region directly in front of or in the immediate neighborhood of this village.

**Summary of coastal diving stations (from north to south)**

| Locality | Comments |
|---|---|
| Ikombe | |
| Nkanda | |
| Lumbira | |
| Kirondo | directly at Kirondo and on the rocky coasts to the north and south |
| Makonde | |
| Lupingu | directly at Lupingu and the rocky coast to the north |
| Magunga | |
| Cove Mountain | |
| Manda | rocky coast north of Manda |
| Ndumbi Reef | reef in the bay of Ndumbi |
| Pombo Reef | rocky reef in front of Pombo |
| Lundu | southern rocky coast |
| Njambe | northern coast |
| Tumbi Rocks | rock formations in front of Tumbi and Tumbi Point |
| Tumbi Reef | rocky reef south of Tumbi Rocks |
| Puulu | rocky coast north of Puulu |
| Puulu Island | western shore |
| Hongi Island | western and eastern shore |
| Mbahwa Island | eastern shore |
| Lundo Island | southwest tip and eastern shore |
| Mbamba Bay | northern rocky coast, pontoon, Luhuchi Rocks, Maunyuni Rocks, southern rocky coast |
| Mara Rocks (Mbamba Bay) | |
| Ngkuyo Island (Mbamba Bay) | western and southern shore |
| Undu Point | |
| Hai Reef | |

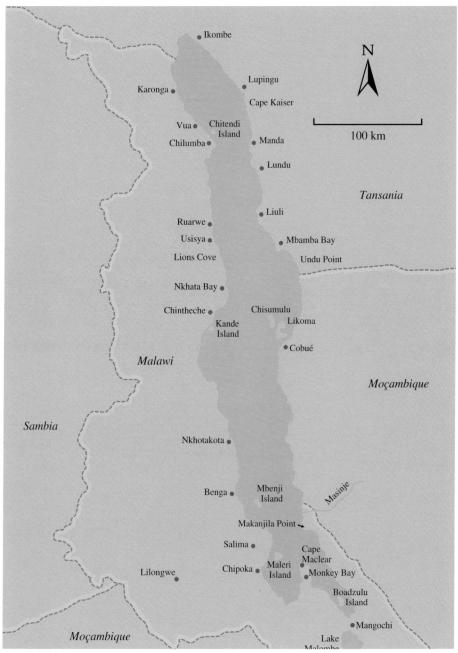

Lake Malawi

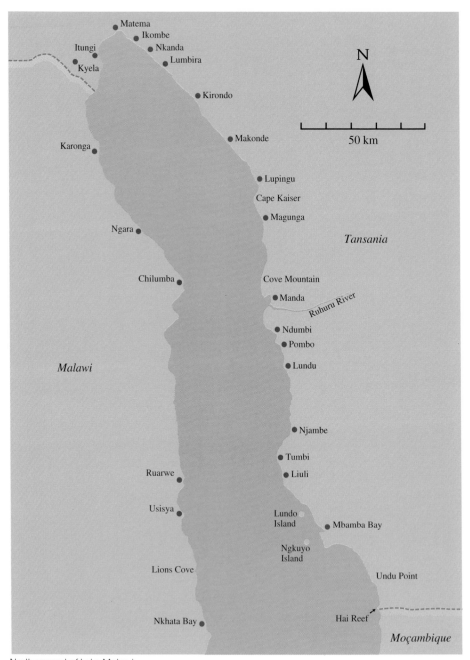

Northern part of Lake Malawi.

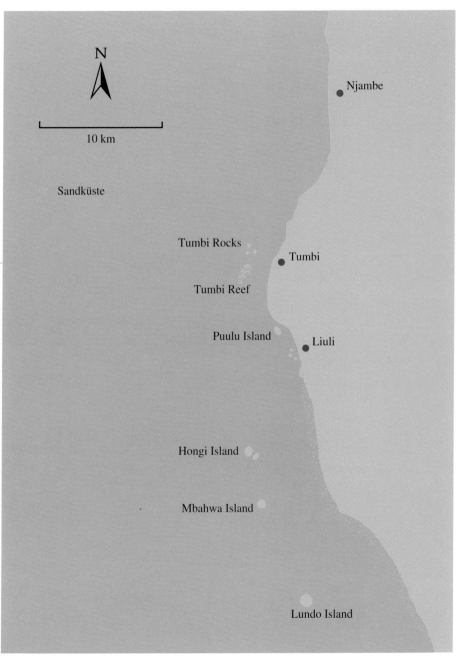

Liuli and adjacent coastal region (note: shore line and distances are estimated; Sandküste = sandy beach).

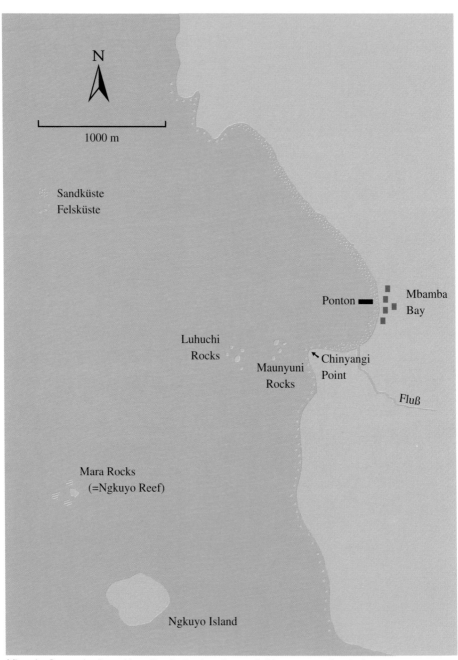

N

1000 m

Sandküste
Felsküste

Ponton ▬ Mbamba
Bay

Luhuchi
Rocks

Maunyuni
Rocks

Chinyangi
Point

Fluß

Mara Rocks
(=Ngkuyo Reef)

Ngkuyo Island

Mbamba Bay and adjacent localities (note: shore line and distances are estimated;
Sandküste = sandy beach; Felsküste = rocky beach; Ponton = pontoon; Fluß = river).

24

# The coast

The northeastern shore of Lake Malawi (called Lake Nyasa in Tanzania) belonging to Tanzania extends over a coastline of approx. 300 kilometers in length.

A small section on the northwestern shore also belongs to Tanzania, but one can ignore the upper point of the lake from Malawi's border to Matema on the northeastern coast (about 40 km) because here the coast is characterized by sandy to muddy shores. The water is predominantly murky so that diving and other forms of underwater observations are scarcely possible.

## Matema to Manda

Extending from Matema to Manda, i.e., about half of the Tanzanian coast of Lake Malawi, there are the Livingstone Mountains, located directly on the lake. These gigantic mountains rising up to 3000 m, as seen from the lake, form a unique and magnificent backdrop. The Livingstone Mountains shape this coastal section both above and under the water. Narrow foot paths run along the slopes and provide the only overland connection between the small villages located onshore. Wide sandy beaches are absent between Matema and Manda.

The following villages are located along this stretch of coast (from north to south): Matema, Ikombe, Nkanda, Lumbira, Makonde, Lupingu, and Manda. Another well-known location is Cape Kaiser, south of Lupingu. One problem with using the villages as points of orientation is that it is difficult to say where a village begins or ends. Many of the small settlements stretch out over long distances along the shore. One way out of this dilemma is to take the churches — built in many villages during German colonial rule under considerable effort

by missionaries (all materials had to be transported by manpower over narrow foot paths) — as the center of a settlement. Furthermore, the church roofs, depending on the angle, reflect the sun so that they can be seen from far away, thus serving as an orientation aid from the lake. There are no large settlements between Lupingu and Manda, but of course even the smallest villages have names which can be learned from the nearly ubiquitous fishermen (for example, Magunga).

Some small rivers, of which during the dry season (roughly from September to November) only the dried-out beds can be seen, flow into the lake, for example, at Lumbira (the former Alt-Langenburg). The rivers often carry the same name as the villages in whose vicinity they enter the lake. None of these small rivers form enough of a barrier to have brought about the development of completely different cichlid communities to the north or south of their estuaries. The same holds for the only large-sized sand bay along this coastal section where the village of Lupingu is located. It seems that this sand bay also failed to serve as a geographical barrier that could have led to the formation of different populations in the adjacent biotopes — at least up to now.

Under water the shoreline usually slopes very steeply, and one virtually dives down the fluted slopes of the Livingstone Mountains. At some locations (for example, north of Lupingu), one can find underwater gorges with rock walls that drop almost vertically to depths of 40 m. Nevertheless — and this is similar to the coast of Malawi — at depths greater than 40 m we could no longer find a purely rocky bottom but sandy and sometimes muddy ground. The bot-

The shore at Ikombe was our most northerly diving site.

Livingstone Mountains at Nkanda; on the right my diving partner Mattayo Jackson.

Nkanda: narrow foot paths provide the only overland connection between the costal villages.

tom continued to slope steeply beyond the 50 m limit, which we did not dare exceed for safety reasons.

But aside from these steeply shelving coastal regions there are also more or less gently sloping shorelines. These are not nearly as rare as one would assume judging by the continuous range of mountains bordering the shore. Small, sandy bays, sometimes containing *Vallisneria* beds, are just as frequent as are shallow sand and stone mixed habitats. At Ikombe and Nkanda, for example, the bottom is primarily sandy, interspersed by only a few stones and rocks. At Lumbira one can also find intermediate zones next to purely rocky habitats. The area north of Kirondo consists of a broad and shallow sandy area with only a few boulders. At depths of ca 6 to 8 m the underwater landscape passes into a more steeply sloping zone with small and medium-sized stones without any sandy areas in between. This is followed at ca 20 m by a somewhat more gently sloping sandy bottom with a few large rocks.

Contrary to appearances, the underwater landscape at the foot of the Livingstone Mountains does not consist entirely of bare and steeply sloping cliffs, but contains, with the exception of spacious sand shores and reed zones, the same diverse biotopes that are familiar from other regions of the lake. However, owing to the extensive rocky or stony regions, the coast between Matema and Manda appears uniform with respect to many cichlid species. That means many species and populations which we found in the extreme north at Ikombe or Nkanda are also distributed at Lupingu or along the coast north of Manda. Offshore islands favoring the development of a specific cichlid fauna of their own are lacking.

## Manda to Lundo Island

As seen from the north, the Livingstone Mountains border the lake only as far as Manda. At Manda, the mountain range turns away from the lake and towards the interior in an easterly direction; later it again runs parallel to the lake, though not as close, and then gradually diminishes in a southerly direction.

Manda is situated on a beautiful sand bay. There are no rocky or stony areas here. Only on the northern edge of the village can one find the rocky coasts of the Livingstone mountains, where we carried out some diving excursions. A long, sandy beach stretches south of Manda, bordered by the estuary of the Ruhuru. The spelling, by the way, is not uniform. "Ruhulu" or "Luhulu" are also common (cf. the preceding chapter on Places and maps).

The Ruhuru is the only large river on the Tanzanian side of the lake. Its delta contains side arms which with their bulrushes and exuberant vegetation are a paradise for birds (and also for crocodiles). Here, the lake water is enriched for long stretches with suspended matter and therefore very murky. Based on our observations, the Ruhuru forms a dividing line between different species or populations, whereby we have primarily the Mbunas in mind, not so much the "Haplochromis" (now known as "Non-Mbunas"), whose affinity for rocky habitats in general is not quite as strong as that of the Mbunas. Travelling south from Manda through the Ruhuru delta for approximately 20 km, one reaches Ndumbi. The shore between Manda and Ndumbi consists of sandy beaches. The first rock formation on this apparently uniform sandy substrate is Pombo Reef. Some rocks jut out from the water so that this location, a few hundred meters offshore, cannot be overlooked. However, this first impression was deceptive, for after a long search we found in Ndumbi Bay an area with underwater rocks (at least 40 by 40 m) located at a depth of about 5 m and extending in the direction of the center of the lake. Owing to the strong deposits of

The shore south of Lumbira.

Rocky shore north of Kirondo.

sediment, this reef (Ndumbi Reef) was not recognizable at first glance from the surface. Furthermore, the vast sandy beaches and the shallow water gave no indication that a reef existed in this bay. This only shows how easy it is to err if one attempts to judge the coastal regions with regard to underwater biotopes by looking at the shore and the color of the water.

From Pombo Reef it is only a few kilometers to Lundu, the next village in a southerly direction. Between Pombo Reef and Lundu the shore is sandy, and we found no other reefs in this area. Like Manda, Lundu lies on a sand bay. The nights in Lundu were characterized by stormy winds coming down from the Livingstone Mountains and whipping through the valley in which Lundu is located. For native fishermen these stormy nights were nothing new; we, however, almost lost our boat during the first night. Fortunately for us, the drifting anchor got caught in a lost fishing net which had become entangled between some rocks south of Lundu. With a borrowed dug-out we were able to retrieve it and to continue our journey.

Another bay is situated south of Lundu, but with rocky shores and corresponding rocky littoral. The rocks, sometimes several cubic meters in size, reach down to depths of 20 to 30 m; below that, we found pure sandy bottom which sloped further downwards.

Njambe lies about 30 km south on a small bay with a sandy beach. The trip from Lundu to Njambe passed shallow, sandy shores. We were unable to determine whether rocky underwater habitats exist between these two villages. To the north, Njambe is bordered by a small bay which is surrounded by rocks. Our diving excursions revealed that the habitats here are, nevertheless, primarily sandy and that only a few solitary rocks exist under water.

Tumbi is located about 10 km south of Njambe. This village has an offshore reef with a shallow part from which some rocks emerge above the water line (Tumbi Rocks). Further south, the reef passes into deeper water, reaching at least 40 m, and is interspersed with some sandy zones (Tumbi Reef). Accordingly, this area should be classified as an intermediate habitat. At Tumbi Rocks the coastline juts out into the lake so that an exposed area results. We observed that especially in the afternoon relatively strong currents prevailed. It was only in the morning that water visibility was what could be called good (more than 10 to 15 m in horizontal direction); in the afternoon, stirred-up sediment made the water murky. Fish density was very high. We observed, for example, a school of at least one hundred individuals from the *Pseudotropheus tropheops* species-group (these species are also considered a species-complex). We furthermore found large swarms of a *Petrotilapia* sp. (*Petrotilapia* "Pointed Head"), one individual close to the other in the current or grazing on the algal mat.

From Tumbi, via Puulu and Puulu Island, one reaches Liuli, one of the larger centers on the northeastern coast. The shores in this coastal section are mostly rocky. The first large-sized bay north of Puulu is also surrounded by boulders on its northern border. Underwater, starting at 5 m, a level intermediate area prevails, i.e., the bay is generally rather shallow (as far as we could judge, based on our diving). At the outer rim of the bay the littoral probably slopes more steeply. Puulu Island is a small island close to the coast. All islands on the Tanzanian coast are uninhabited. On the side facing the lake, a relatively broad strip of intermediate zones can be found. This stretch of shore slopes gradually to depths of over 40 m. At ca 10 m the underwater landscape changed. Large rocks prevailed and not until after about 30 to 35 m does one again find any sandy ground between the rocks, i.e., here the rocks give way slowly to a deep

Stupendous scenery: the Livingstone Mountains south of Kirondo.

Steeply sloping shore north of Makonde.

31

sandy zone. At this depth fish density was comparatively low, but that applies in principle to many localities.

Liuli has a mission station with a hospital and several stores. After Manda, Liuli is the next of the three large-sized villages along the northeastern coast. The third important village is Mbamba Bay (see below) to the south. Liuli has an ideal natural harbor. The relatively deep cut of the bay offers natural protection against storms. Towards the south, however, the bay is relatively open, but at the southern rim there are several small islands and rocks, screening Liuli from the lake. The best known island or rather the best known rock is Sphinx Rock (Sphinx Island). This rock formation, located at the entry to the harbor, resembles the Sphinx of Gizeh in Egypt, that mixed configuration with the body of a lion and the head of a king. Another old name for Liuli is therefore Sphinx Haven. Since this oriental mythical beast is not that well known among the inhabitants of Liuli, it shouldn't surprise anyone that there is also a "native" name for this rock formation: Pomonda (Rock) is the term used by the locals.

More rocks and a shallow bay surrounded by bulrushes follow directly south of Liuli. This combination, bulrushes and numerous rocks with hiding places, seems to be ideal for crocodiles. Liuli is (or was) well known for its crocodiles. For centuries, people here lived with the knowledge that death lived next door. According to native tales, people, in particular children, were killed on a nearly regular basis. This was accepted as fate; nobody knew otherwise. Until this day, magic and witchcraft surround these crocodiles and those who claim to control them. Only recently, at the beginning of the nineties, did things change. A "Mzungu" or white man had become the victim of a crocodile. Armed with goggles and fins he had his mind set on exploring precisely that rocky region in which

— as was well known — a large croc had his territory. Whether recklessness or ignorance were to blame, the death of a "Mzungu" made waves and the death of the crocs, including the murderous one, followed. It is said that more than 40 crocodiles lost their lives to steel hooks, baited with dog or goat meat. Since then Liuli is said to be a croc-free zone.

A well-known island a few kilometers south of Liuli is Hongi (*Labidochromis* "Hongi"). Hongi is a "double island". Two collections of large boulders emerge from the water close together. Another, but smaller rock formation is located south of Hongi Island, called Mbahwa Island. At Hongi as well as at Mbahwa only the shallow shore littoral consists of large boulders. At the places where we dived, at a depth of roughly 8 to 15 m, exclusively mixed ground existed. Here the number of rocks and also the bottom slope decreased and sandy zones dominated the underwater landscape.

From Liuli to Lundo Islands the coast is comparatively shallow with long sandy beaches. Aside from Hongi and Mbahwa Island there are, however, more rock formations. A number of rocks jut out from the water between Mbahwa and Lundo Island. It is possible that several reefs also exist.

Lundo Island, together with Ngkuyo Island (see below), are the two largest islands on Tanzanian territory. Biotopes around the large islands are diverse. The southwestern shore of Lundo Island consists of purely rocky or stony areas, sloping steeply to depths of 30 m. But on the eastern side, facing the mainland, one can find moderately sloping mixed habitats giving way to sandy areas in deeper water.

## From Mbamba Bay to the border of Mozambique

Mbamba Bay, the best known town on the Tanzanian side of Lake Malawi, is the starting point

Northern bay of Lupingu.

Manda is situated on a long sandy beach.

33

At Pombo Reef, we discovered several new species.

Northern part of the Njambe bay.

Rocky shore north of Puulu.

Mbamba Bay beach, one of the few large villages on the southern coast.

35

for most people that travel the southern coast. As the name implies, Mbamba Bay is located in a large inlet. Rocky habitats surround the bay on both the northern and the southern side.

With regard to cichlid biotopes, the southern region of Mbamba Bay is of great interest. Chinyanga Point is located on the southern border and consists of a number of rocks which are partially submerged. The two most striking rock formations, according to native accounts, are called Luhuchi Rocks and Maunyuni Rocks. Also south of Mbamba Bay is Ngkuyo Island, sometimes also called Mbamba Bay Island. This island is separated from the mainland by relatively large depths. Some endemic cichlid populations seem to have evolved here. North of Ngkuyo Island a deeply sloping reef is located: Mara Rocks (occasionally also called Ngkuyo Rocks or Ngkuyo Reef). The tip of this reef juts out from the water as a rock of about 2 cubic meters (1993), thus making it easy to find. At all these locations, immense rocks, mostly comprising several cubic meters, dominate the underwater landscape. Only at greater depths do open sandy areas of different dimensions occur.

After the southern rocky coast of Mbamba Bay, a sandy beach of about 40 km covers the distance to the border of Mozambique. Undu, a small isolated rocky region, is located half-way down the beach. Here we found interesting cichlid populations in intermediate habitats at about 5 to 10 m.

A comparable biotope exists just north of the border of Mozambique, not far from the village of Ngombo. The small reef, consisting of rocks or large stones, is called "Hai Reef" (pronounced "why"). This mixed area slopes very gently and most cichlids here live in depths of ca 5 to 15 m. Hai Reef was our southern- most diving station.

The southern most region of Mbamba Bay is called Chinyanga Point.

Long sandy beaches are typical for the coast south of Undu Point.

# Survey of species in tabular form

We were able to find many of the well-known species from Malawi in the course of our investigations. In the following tabular survey all species that caught our attention are summarized. Cichlids that are easily classified within a genus, but not with respect to their species are not listed. This pertains primarily to the genera *Copadichromis, Nyassachromis, Diplotaxodon,* and *Rhamphochromis,* of which we repeatedly (sometimes even in large numbers) observed specimens or found them in the catch of native fishermen. It goes without saying that this species list makes no claims to completeness. The tabular survey is divided into two parts: Non-Mbunas and Mbunas. If similar populations are known from Malawi, this will be noted under Comments. The expression "similar" does not mean that the different populations belong to the same species, but merely suggests possible close relationships.

The predatory *Rhamphochromis* spp. grow to more than 40 cm in size and are especially prized for their delicious taste.

## 1. Species list of Non-Mbunas

| Genus/Species | Comments |
|---|---|
| *Aristochromis* | |
| *christyi* | Widely distributed. |
| *Auloncara* | |
| "Chitendi Type Tanzania" | Probably conspecific populations are known from Malawi's east coast, Makanjila/Fort Maguire (*A.* "Chitendi Type East Coast"). |
| *jacobfreibergi* | Also known from Malawi's east coast (Makanjila) and several localities from the south of the lake (Cape Maclear and others). |
| "Lupingu" | Only known from Tanzania. Similar populations known from Malawi's east coast (Makanjila/Fort Maguire). |
| "Mamelela" | Only known from Tanzania. |
| *rostratum* | Known from several coastal regions of Malawi, possibly widely distributed. |
| cf. *saulosi* | Very similar to *A.* "Greenface Metallic", which could be a geographic race of *A. saulosi*. |
| *steveni* | Probably widely distributed. In Tanzania several local forms. |
| "Yellow Top" | Only known from Tanzania. |
| *Buccochromis* | |
| *heterotaenia* | Widely distributed. |
| *lepturus* | Widely distributed. |
| *rhoadesii* | Widely distributed. |
| *Champsochromis* | |
| *caeruleus* | Widely distributed. |
| *Cheilochromis* | |
| *euchilus* | Widely distributed. |
| *Chilotilapia* | |
| *rhoadesii* | Widely distributed. |
| *Copadichromis* | |
| *borleyi* | Widely distributed. |
| *chrysonotus* | Widely distributed. |
| "Fire Crest Wimpel" | Also known from the east coast of Malawi (Makanjila/ Fort Maguire). |
| "Fire Crest Yellow" | Also known from the east coast of Malawi (Makanjila/ Fort Maguire). |
| cf. *flavimanus* | Probably widely distributed. |

| Genus/Species | Comments |
|---|---|

"Mloto White Top" — Conspecific, but slightly different colored populations are known from Likoma Island and Chisumulu Island.

*jacksoni* — Widely distributed.

cf. *pleurostigma* — The only type specimen of *C. pleurostigma* stems from Chilumba. It is possible that this species is only distributed in the northern part of the lake.

cf. *prostoma* — Widely distributed.

"Verduyni Deep Blue" — Probably a geographical form (subspecies) of *C. verduyni*.

"Verduyni Northern" — Probably a geographical form (subspecies) of *C. verduyni*.

**Corematodus**
*taeniatus* — Widely distributed.

**Ctenopharynx**
*nitidus* — Widely distributed.
*pictus* — Widely distributed.

**Cyrtocara**
*moorii* — Widely distributed.

**Dimidiochromis**
*kiwinge* — Widely distributed.
*strigatus* — Widely distributed.

**Docimodus**
*evelynae* — Widely distributed.

**Eclectochromis**
*milomo* — Widely distributed.
*ornatus* — Widely distributed.

**Exochochromis**
*anagenys* — Widely distributed.

**Fossorochromis**
*rostratus* — Widely distributed.

**Hemitaeniochromis**
*urotaenia* — Widely distributed.

**Hemitilapia**
*oxyrhynchus* — Widely distributed.

**Lethrinops**
"Yellow Collar" — Widely distributed.

**Lichnochromis**
*acuticeps* — Widely distributed.

**Mylochromis**
*labidodon* — Widely distributed.

| Genus/Species | Comments |
|---|---|

"Mchuse"  
Only known from Tanzania.

*mola*  
Widely distributed.

"Pointed Head Tanzania"  
A very similar population lives along Malawi's east coast (Makanjila/Fort Maguire; trade name: *M.* "Pointed Head" or *M.* "Makanjila Mola").

*semipalatus*  
Widely distributed.

**Nimbochromis**

*linni*  
Widely distributed.

*livingstonii*  
Widely distributed.

*polystigma*  
Widely distributed.

**Nyassachromis**

"Yellow Head"  
Only known from Tanzania.

**Otopharynx**

"Big Spot Tanzania"  
Similar populations are known from Malawi. Probably close relationship to *O. heterodon*, perhaps even the same species is involved. A very similar, possibly conspecific population from the island of Chisumulu has been offered commercially under the name of *O.* "Royal Blue".

"Blue Yellow Tanzania"  
Only known from Tanzania.

**Placidochromis**

"Electra Blue Hongi"  
Only known from Tanzania.

"Electra Makonde"  
Only known from Tanzania.

*johnstoni*  
Widely distributed.

"Johnstoni Solo"  
Known from a few coastal regions of Malawi (e.g., Chisumulu).

cf. *phenochilus*  
So far *P. phenochilos* is only known from the northern part of the lake.

**Protomelas**

*annectens*  
Widely distributed, but rare species.

*fenestratus*  
Widely distributed, with many local forms in Tanzania.

"Fenestratus Taiwan"  
Probably a subspecies of *P. fenestratus*. A nearly identical population is known from Taiwan Reef at Chisumulu.

"Fenestratus Ngkuyo"  
Probably local form of *P.* "Fenestratus Taiwan". The only difference consists in the coloration of the anal fin (yellow instead of red).

cf. *pleurotaenia*  
*P. pleurotaenia* is probably widely distributed.

| Genus/Species | Comments |
|---|---|
| *spilonotus* | Widely distributed. |
| "Spilonotus Tanzania" | Only known from Tanzania. |
| *spilopterus* | Widely distributed. |
| "Spilopterus Blue" | Widely distributed. |
| **Sciaenochromis** | |
| *fryeri* | Widely distributed. |
| **Stigmatochromis** | |
| "Cave" | Probably widely distributed. |
| *modestus* | Widely distributed. Rare along Malawi's coast; occurs relatively frequently in Tanzania. |
| *pholidophorus* | Probably widely distributed, but nowhere frequent. Occurs relatively often along Malawi's east coast (Makanjila/Fort Maguire). |
| *woodi* | Widely distributed. |
| **Taenichromis** | |
| *holotaenia* | Widely distributed. |
| **Taeniolethrinops** | |
| "Black Fin" | Probably widely distributed. |
| *praeorbitalis* | Widely distributed. |
| **Tramitichromis** | |
| cf. *brevis* | Probably widely distributed. |
| **Trematocranus** | |
| *placodon* | Widely distributed. |
| **Tyrannochromis** | |
| *macrostoma* | Widely distributed. |
| *nigriventer* | Widely distributed. Melanin pattern of northern population clearly differs from that in populations living south of Nkhata Bay and at Likoma/Chisumulu. |

## 2. Species list for Mbunas

| Genus/Species | Comments |
|---|---|
| *Cyathochromis* | |
| *obliquidens* | Widely distributed. |
| *Cynotilapia* | |
| *afra* | Widely distributed. Many new populations in Tanzania. |
| "Lion" | Also known from the northwest coast. Populations from the northwest and northeast coast display different dorsal fin coloration. |
| *Genyochromis* | |
| *mento* | Widely distributed. |
| *Gephyrochromis* | |
| "Yellow" | Only known from Tanzania. Relationship to *G. lawsi* needs to be examined. |
| *Labeotropheus* | |
| *fuelleborni* | Widely distributed. Many local forms are known. |
| *trewavasae* | Widely distributed. Many local forms are known. A unique form was found at Ngkuyo Island (Mbamba Bay). |
| *Labidochromis* | |
| "Black Dorsal" | Only known from Tanzania. |
| "Blue/White" | Only known from Tanzania. |
| "Blunt Nose" | Only known from Tanzania. |
| "Deep Body" | Only known from Tanzania. |
| "Hongi" | Only known from Tanzania. |
| "Luhuchi" | Only known from Tanzania. |
| *maculicauda* | Also occurs along northwest coast. |
| "Perlmutt" | Only known from Tanzania. |
| "Red Top Mbamba Bay" | Only known from Tanzania. |
| *Melanochromis* | |
| "Blue" | Also occurs along northwest coast and at Likoma. |
| "Northern" | Only known from Tanzania. |
| *parallelus* | Also occurs along northwest coast and at Likoma and Chisumulu. |
| *"Melanochromis"* | |
| *labrosus* | Widely distributed, but rare species. Occurs relatively frequently in Tanzania. |
| *Petrotilapia* | |
| "Pointed Head" | Only known from Tanzania. Similar populations live in Malawi. |

| Genus/Species | Comments |
| --- | --- |

"Tanzania"                Only known from Tanzania. Similar populations live in
                          Malawi.
*tridentiger*             Widely distributed.
**Pseudotropheus**
   "Aggressive Puulu"     Only known from Tanzania.
   "Black Dorsal Tanzania"   Similar populations are known from the south of the lake
                          (Thumbi West Island, Chindunga Reef, Maleri Islands).
   "Broad Bar"            Only known from Tanzania.
   *crabro*               Widely distributed.
   "Daktari"              Only known from Tanzania. A similar species is *P.*
                          "Lime" from Likoma.
   *demasoni*             Only known from Tanzania.
   "Dolphin"              Only known from Tanzania.
   "Livingstoni Likoma"   Known from Likoma.
   "Msobo"                Only known from Tanzania. A similar population lives at
                          Likoma (*P.* "Membe Deep").
   "Orange Cap"           Only known from Tanzania.
   "Plain"                Only known from Tanzania.
   "Pombo Yellow Breast"  Only known from Tanzania.
   "Red Top Ndumbi"       Only known from Tanzania.
   *tursiops*             Other populations of this species live at Chisumulu and
                          along the northwest coast.
   "Variable Tanzania"    Only known from Tanzania. Possibly related species live
                          along the northwest coast.
   *williamsi*            Members of the *P. williamsi* species-complex inhabit
                          large regions of the lake.
   "Yellow Tail"          Only known from Tanzania.
**P. elongatus species-group**
   "Elongatus Deep Water" Only known from Tanzania.
   "Elongatus Luhuchi"    Only known from Tanzania.
   "Elongatus Mbamba"     Only known from Tanzania.
   "Elongatus Ngkuyo"     Only known from Tanzania.
   "Elongatus Robust"     Only known from Tanzania.
   "Elongatus Sand"       Only known from Tanzania.
   "Elongatus Spot"       Only known from Tanzania.
**P. tropheops species-group**
   "Tropheops Big Blue Yellow"  Only known from Tanzania. Very similar populations live
                          in Malawi.
   "Tropheops Checkered"  Only known from Tanzania.
   "Tropheops Chilumba"   Already sighted at Chilumba.

44

| Genus/Species | Comments |
|---|---|
| "Tropheops Chitande Yellow" | Known from northwest coast at Chilumba. |
| "Tropheops Mbamba" | Only known from Tanzania. Similar populations in Malawi. |
| "Tropheops Mutant" | Only known from Tanzania. |
| "Tropheops Olive" | Also sighted along northwest coast. |
| "Tropheops Red Fin" | Widely distributed along northwest coast. |
| "Tropheops Rusty Hongi" | Only known from Tanzania. Similar populations were seen in Malawi. |
| "Tropheops Sand" | Only known from Tanzania. |
| "Tropheops Weed Tanzania" | A possibly conspecific population from the northwest coast is known as *P.* "Tropheops Weed". |
| "Tropheops Yellow Head" | Only known from Tanzania. Similar populations live in Malawi. |

**P. *zebra* species-complex**

| | |
|---|---|
| *callainos* | Wide distribution, also on northwest coast. |
| *fainzilberi* | Only known from Tanzania. |
| *zebra* | Widely distributed. Several local forms occur in Tanzania. |
| "Zebra Blue Gold" | Only known from Tanzania. |
| "Zebra Dwarf Tanzania" | Only known from Tanzania. |
| "Zebra Gold Breast Mbamba" | Only known from Tanzania. |
| "Zebra Gold Breast Orange Top" | Only known from Tanzania. |
| "Zebra Mbamba Bay Kompakt" | Only known from Tanzania. |
| "Zebra Slim" | Only known from Tanzania. |
| "Zebra South" | Only known from Tanzania. |
| "Zebra Yellow Belly" | Only known from Tanzania. |

# Non-Mbunas

The overwhelming majority of Lake Malawi cichlids can be divided into two groups: Mbunas and Non-Mbunas. In the past the term "Haplochromis" was also used for Non-Mbunas, which, however, is no longer available owing to new taxonomic classifications (for further details see below). Consequently, we are left with the unusual-sounding expression "Non-Mbuna", which requires further explanation. The relatively small Mbunas are strictly rock-associated and can generally be classified as specialized feeders of Aufwuchs (epilithic algae). In contrast, most Non-Mbunas do not exhibit this strict connection with the stony (rocky) bottom, are larger and with respect to feeding can be described as less specialized omnivores. For a definition of the Mbuna group see the preliminary text of the special chapter on Mbunas.

Presently there are about 250 known species of Non-Mbunas, which are divided into 38 genera. Most of the genera are defined on the basis of melanin patterns (see below). The total length of Non-Mbunas lies roughly between 10 and 40 cm; most species grow to about 15 cm and only a few genera exhibit a total length of over 30 cm. While the coloration of females and fry is mostly inconspicuous, dominant and sexually active males develop marvelous blue, green, and even black coloration. All species are maternal mouthbrooders and are endemic to Lake Malawi. A few species have been found in the Shire River and in Lake Malombe. The Shire drains Lake Malawi in the south and flows into Lake Malombe.

The Non-Mbunas have gained access to every biotope and exploit practically every food source. One can find all transitional forms: from a more or less nonspecialized omnivore, feeder on micro-organisms or fish predator, to the extreme specialists such as scale and fin eaters. Despite this diversity of forms and feeding habits one can nevertheless recognize some ecological groups. In the first place we must mention the "Utaka". According to the native fishermen of Malawi, Utaka are those cichlids which have adapted to a way of life in open water and, equipped with a tube-like, bulging mouth, feed primarily on plankton. Presently the Utaka are summarized in the genus *Copadichromis*; however, it is likely that this genus contains several evolutionary lineages, so it is foreseeable that future classification work will result in several genera. There is also some overlapping with the genus *Nyassachromis*, which contains elongated cichlids that favor sandy bottoms. Predatory inhabitants of open or deep water are represented by the genera *Rhamphochromis* and *Diplotaxodon*. Another group of sand-dwelling cichlids are the representatives of the genera *Lethrinops*, *Taeniolethrinops,* and *Tramitichromis* (in the past all of them denoted as *Lethrinops*), which specialize in looking for their prey in the substrate. To this end they pick up portions of sand and sieve it carefully. Fish predators can be found in many genera and with certainty do not form a natural unit but in evolutionary terms have developed in multiple ways.

It would go beyond the existing framework to give more details on these diverse specializations. We refer the reader to the pertinent literature (for an overview: Fryer & Iles 1972, Eccles & Trewavas 1989).

The following 38 genera form the group of Non-Mbunas (in alphabetical order):

*Alticorpus*
*Aristochromis*
*Aulonocara*
*Buccochromis*
*Caprichromis*
*Champsochromis*
*Cheilochromis*
*Chilotilapia*
*Copadichromis*
*Corematodus*
*Ctenopharynx*
*Cyrtocara*
*Dimidiochromis*
*Diplotaxodon*
*Docimodus*
*Eclectochromis*
*Exochochromis*
*Fossorochromis*
*Hemitaeniochromis*
*Hemitilapia*
*Lethrinops*
*Lichnochromis*
*Mylochromis*
    (previously *Maravichromis*)
*Naevochromis*
*Nimbochromis*
*Nyassachromis*
*Otopharynx*
*Placidochromis*
*Platygnathochromis*
*Protomelas*
*Rhamphochromis*
*Sciaenochromis*
*Stigmatochromis*
*Taeniochromis*
*Taeniolethrinops*
*Tramitichromis*
*Trematocranus*
*Tyrannochromis*

## Explanations on classification

Until 1989 nearly all cichlids of Lake Malawi were lumped together as either Mbunas or "Haplochromis". In addition, some other genera were known that included Non-Mbunas, and these were also included among the "Haplochromis" relations (for example, *Aristochromis*, *Aulonocara*).

The expression "Haplochromis" — note the quotation marks — can be traced to the fact that during the first half of this century many species of the Non-Mbunas were placed in the genus *Haplochromis*. At that time, this genus included numerous species from other African countries, among them riverine cichlids. As more and more cichlids became known, it became obvious that the genus *Haplochromis* no longer formed a natural unit, but had become a "collective genus" for many species. (Taxonomy or systematic ordering should always consider the evolution of the respective species, i.e., in principle, it should reflect the phylogenetic tree of the species.) At the end of the 1970s the genus *Haplochromis* was revised and limited to a few species. Most of the previous *Haplochromis* spp. were distributed among newly established genera (GREENWOOD 1979, 1980), but the Lake Malawi *Haplochromis* were not addressed at all in the framework of this research project. So while the genus *Haplochromis* was now limited to a few species, the "Lake Malawi Haps" group, as these cichlids were known in short, were, from a systematic viewpoint, suddenly without a valid genus name and thus were denoted as "Haplochromis" — in quotation marks — to indicate that the genus name was not verified and in need of revision.

In 1989, ECCLES and TREWAVAS provided this revision of the former Lake Malawi *Haplochromis*. They described 23 new genera so as to order the more than 100 species according to their natural relationships. Another 15 "old" genera, which even then denoted "Haplochromis" relatives, were also revised and newly defined, so that the group of Non-Mbunas now contains all these 38 genera. Owing to this revision of the "Haplochromis", this term is no longer valid, and for semantic reasons only the term "Non-Mbuna" is presently used. (Not included in the division into Mbunas and Non-Mbunas are the few *Tilapia*, *Oreochromis*, and *Serranochromis* spp. as well as *Astatotilapia calliptera*. The closest relatives of these species are to be found among the less specialized riverine cichlids, thus they exhibit other evolutionary "roots" than the true lake-dwelling cichlids. Furthermore, it has to be kept in mind that the expression Non-Mbuna pertains only to Lake Malawi cichlids and contains the above exceptions.)

It must be emphasized that a crucial step in this revision is the fact that the new classification is no longer based on the old criteria of traditional morphological and morphometric features (dentition, fin structure, number of scales, etc.). Rather many species are very similar in this regard and transitions are fluid so that a division into distinct genera based on these criteria would have been hard to justify. But, much more important was the conclusion of Eccles and Trewavas that morphological structures are strongly influenced by the environment, and thus, in simplified terms, are less representative of phylogenetic relationships than an adaptation to the respective environmental conditions. As an example, the parallel (convergent) evolution of the specialized teeth of snail eaters which, owing to this feature, are distinguished from other cichlids as an "artificial" group, although they are not related to each other. Such parallel developments are meaningless for any phylogenetic classification (phylogeny = evolutionary history of species).

Thus, since it was impossible to classify these phylogenetically young species on the basis of the above morphological characteristics, the question of other criteria arose. As a crucial criterion the basic melanin pattern was selected. The melanin pattern is the basic black pigmentation (most easily recognizable in females and juveniles), which should not be confused with coloration that is variable in many species. In contrast to morphological features, it appears to be easier to recognize phylogenetic relationships based on melanin patterning, since melanin patterns are evidently less influenced by environmental factors.

Altogether seven basic types of melanin pattern are distinguished (for example, strongly marked vertical bars, central (midlateral) longitudinal band, diagonal band or three-spot patterns). For the respective genus-typical patterns, see the genus descriptions.

# The genus *Aulonocara*　　　　　　　　　　REGAN 1922

The representatives of the genus *Aulonocara* (peacock cichlids) are characterized by dimple-like openings in the head area, which are particularly pronounced in the cheeks. These characteristic openings are easy to recognize if one observes *Aulonocara* spp. outside the water in slanted light. These dimples represent enlarged sensory pores of the lateral line system (cephalic lateral line pits) and most likely serve to perceive fluctuations in pressure. It is possible that this remote sense of touch helps the fish to zoom in on prey. A melanin pattern is developed only faintly and consists of vertical bars which, depending on mood, become more or less distinct.

At present, two ecological groups are distinguished (TREWAVAS 1984). The group of sand-dwelling *Aulonocara* comprises relatively large species (total lengths ca 15 cm to 20 cm) which inhabit sandy areas and rarely venture out into mixed habitats. Little is known about this group. The best known species is *Aulonocara rostratum*. *A. macrochir*, which is also ordered in this group (ECCLES 1989b), is probably conspecific with the first-named species. Other sand-dwelling *Aulonocara* are *A. guentheri* and *A. nyassae* (ECCLES 1989b) and possibly also *A. trematocephala*, *A. brevirostris,* and *A. auditor* (SPREINAT 1989c: 22). Here it must be mentioned that the aquaristically best known (at least by name) peacock, *A. nyassae*, with high probability has never been imported live. Species imported in the past, with few exceptions, belong to the group of rock-dwelling *Aulonocara*.

The rock-dwelling peacocks represent the brilliantly colored small species which are highly popular in aquaristic circles. Most species inhabit intermediate zones, a very few prefer large caves as biotope. About 20 species of rock-dwelling *Aulonocara* are known from Malawi. In some cases, it is not clear whether similar looking "forms" that live on different coasts represent independent species or merely local forms of a widely distributed species. Here more research needs to be done.

In Tanzania, we found *A. rostratum* from the group of sand-dwelling *Aulonocara*, a species which is probably distributed throughout the entire lake. We were furthermore able to find *A. jacobfreibergi* (at Hongi Island and Njambe) which also occurs in Malawi, and several local forms of *A. steveni* (see below). Two populations that we observed were very similar to species known from Malawi: *A.* "Chitendi Type Tanzania", which could probably be ordered as conspecific with *A.* "Chitendi Type East Coast" (SPREINAT 1989c) and a population from Hai Reef (*A.* cf. *saulosi*) which is very similar to *A. saulosi* (from Malawi's east coast at Makanjila) or the *A.* "Greenface Metallic" that lives at Likoma Island, which in turn might be classified as subspecies of *A. saulosi*.

Species that so far are only known from Tanzania, are *A.* "Lupingu", *A.* "Mamelela", and *A.* "Yellow Top".

# *Aulonocara* "Lupingu"

## Name

The tentative working name refers to the village of Lupingu where this species can be observed with relative frequency.

## Characteristics

At a total length of ca 12 to 13 cm this is a comparatively large *Aulonocara*. Female: grey with yellow pelvic and anal fins. Male with blue head and usually intensive yellow bar from neck to chest. Depending on population, a yellow coloration expands over the entire flank so that the males, except for the blue head, are yellow to reddish overall (Lupingu population). Males without this yellow flank pigmentation show blue lateral color. Except for the pectoral fins, all fins exhibit dark pigmentations, albeit with different levels of intensity. The dorsal fin shows a white edge and white tips. Anal fin with numerous egg spots, which, however, vary rather strongly with respect to number and size.

## Distribution

Detected at Nkanda, Lumira, Makonde, and Lupingu. Probably widely distributed in the area of the Livingstone Mountains. We could not find this species south of the Ruhuru at any place.

## Habitat and feeding

*A.* "Lupingu" appears to prefer deeper water at about 15 to 40 m. Rarely did we find this species above 10 m. The biotope is formed by a typical intermediate zone (rock/sand interface). Males are solitary and territorial. Females were found solitary or in small groups. *A.* "Lupingu", like most peacock cichlids, feeds on small invertebrates that live in or on the sandy stratum.

## Similar species

Recently, *A.* "Jumbo Blue" has been exported from Malawi (SPREINAT 1992a). These individuals stemmed from Malawi's east coast (area of Makanjila/Fort Maguire). Regarding body shape and size, *A.* "Jumbo Blue" is comparable to *A.* "Lupingu". The females also show yellow pelvic and anal fins. But *A.* "Jumbo Blue", also known under the trade name of *A.* "Multispot", sports no yellow bar behind the gill covers, and only develops relatively weak yellow pigmentation on the back and in the upper flank area.

*Aulonocara* "Jumbo Blue" (Makanjila, aquarium photo)

*Aulonocara* "Lupingu" (Makonde)

*Aulonocara* "Lupingu", female (Makonde)

*Aulonocara* "Lupingu" (Makonde)

*Aulonocara* "Lupingu" (Lupingu)

*Aulonocara* "Lupingu" (Lupingu)

51

# *Aulonocara* "Mamelela"

### Name

This peacock cichlid was introduced in April 1992 under the trade name of "Mamelela" (RUSS 1993).

### Characteristics

At an overall length of ca 10 cm this is a small *Aulonocara* sp. which, due to the pointed head and a body that is rather elongate for this genus, is reminiscent of *A. jacobfreibergi* (previously *Trematocranus jacobfreibergi*). While the usually smaller females sport a grey color with a suggestion of dark bars, the males are strikingly yellow to orange blue. The lower head area up to the operculum is metallic blue. Above the eye and in the suboccipital region, yellow coloration extends via nape and shoulder into the upper dorsal area. Chest and belly are also yellow. The flanks exhibit primarily a blue coloration. Pelvic, dorsal and anal fins show an intensive yellow pigmentation. Some specimens show hues that are more orange than yellow. The dorsal lappets are white to bluish.

### Distribution

*A.* "Mamelela" was only detected at Undu Point. RUSS (1993) reports that according to the divers of an exporter, this fish is said to occur at "Hay Reef" (Hai Reef). We tried in vain to find this species there. At Undu Point, *A.* "Mamelela" occurs with relative frequency.

### Habitat and feeding

Undu Point is a small area with rocks and stones located on the sandy beach of about 40 km length between Mbamba Bay and the border of Mozambique. The rocks continue under water and form a mixed substrate, the majority of which consists of small or medium-sized stones. While *A.* "Mamelela" lives directly between these stones, unlike *A. jacobfreibergi* it does not prefer to hover in caves or rocky crannies. Males are territorial and defend small territories (about 50 cm in diameter), whose center is a stone wall or a stony cranny. We only found solitary females that did not appear to be territorial. Food is obtained from the substrate or from rocks covered by a sedimentary layer. The depth at which we found this species ranged from 5 to 10 m.

### Similar species

As already mentioned, it is very likely that this species is closely related to *A. jacobfreibergi*. *A. jacobfreibergi* was discovered along the east coast of Malawi (JOHNSON 1974). Other populations were later also detected at various places along the coast of Malawi (RIBBINK et al. 1983: 249). We found *A. jacobfreibergi* at Njambe and Hongi Island. Essentially these populations do not differ in coloration from populations at other coastal sections. This indicates that *A.* "Mamelela" is not so much a geographic form or subspecies of *A. jacobfreibergi*, but an independent species. It is remarkable that *A.* "Mamelela" occurs only at Undu Point while other similar biotopes of the adjacent coastal regions are not inhabited by them (or only by very few specimens?).

*Aulonocara* "Mamelela" (Undu Point)

*Aulonocara* "Mamelela" (Undu Point)

53

# *Aulonocara steveni*

### Characteristics

Medium-sized peacock cichlid (overall length 9 to 11 cm) with blue head and yellow body coloration. Comparatively faint pattern of dark vertical bars. Anal fin with variable spots; sometimes numerous large egg spots exist, and sometimes only a few yellow pigment stripes are visible. The intensity of the yellow coloration varies with population. Another feature varying with population concerns the coloring of the dorsal fin. Populations from Njambe to Mbamba Bay clearly show a black submarginal band which stands out prominently against the basic yellow of the dorsal fin. In the populations from Undu Point and Hai Reef, the dorsal fins are mainly blue. All populations sport a white to light-blue edge on their dorsal fin. The coloration of anal fins with regard to the formation of darker pigmentation is also variable. The females are grey to brown with dark vertical bars and, as a rule, cannot be distinguished by population.

### Distribution

This species was discovered on the west coast near Kande Island (MEYER et al. 1987). *A. steveni* was seen by us at Njambe, Tumbi Reef, Mbahwa Island, Mbamba Bay (Pontoon), Undu Point, and Hai Reef. This species is probably distributed over the entire Tanzanian coast south of the Ruhuru estuary. North of the Ruhuru we did not observe *A. steveni*.

### Habitat and feeding

*A. steveni* prefers intermediate zones ranging from shallow water to depths of 20 m. It is rarely found at a greater depth. Males are territori-al, while the females live solitary or in groups and usually linger near the males' territory. At low population densities, it is almost impossible to observe territorial behavior of males. In Mbamba Bay, directly by the pontoon sunk near the beach, a small population lives at a depth of about 5 to 6 m. The wall of the pontoon jutting obliquely out in front offers a kind of shelter. Six males, as little as 50 cm apart, had dug out small shallow holes in the gravelly sand directly at the foot of the pontoon. The territorial males patrolled in front of these shallow depressions. Females and subadults massed around in troops of about 40 to 50 specimens in front of these territories, but at the approach of the diver they also sought the shelter of the pontoon.

*A. steveni* feeds on small invertebrates which are taken from the substrate.

### Similar species

A close relationship exists to *A. stuartgranti* (Chilumba; northwest coast), *A. baenschi* (Nkhomo resp. Benga, Maleri Islands, Chipoka; southwest coast), *A. korneliae* (Chisumulu Island) and *A. hueseri* (Likoma Island). All these species form a close unit in that the males are characterized by mostly contrasting yellow-blue colorations (rarely only one of the two colors). Unfortunately, the classification of populations of the above species, especially of *A. steveni* and *A. stuartgranti* has become rather obscured due to the revision by MEYER et al. (1987) and some aquaristic publications. Essential facts about the species living on the mainland coast are summarized in the following (not including morphological details).

*A. steveni* is essentially characterized by a yellow body, blue head, and black pigmentation

*Aulonocara steveni* (Njambe)

*Aulonocara steveni* (Tumbi Reef)

*Aulonocara steveni* (Mbahwa Island)

*Aulonocara steveni* (Pontoon, Mbamba Bay)

*Aulonocara steveni* (Undu Point)

in the dorsal fins. The type locality (locality of the type specimens) is Kande Island. *A. baenschi* is also yellow with blue head, but exhibits no black or blue coloration in the dorsal fin. Its type locality is Benga (Nkhomo Reef). *A. stuartgranti* is an completely blue cichlid sporting small amounts of yellow on the flanks. The dorsal fin is mostly blue, rarely with black pigmentation. Type locality is Chilumba. The populations living on the northeast coast of Tanzania, with regard to the characteristics described above, correspond to *A. steveni*. Consequently, these populations are classified as *A. steveni*. The occurrence on the northwest coast, between the type locations of *A. steveni* and *A. stuartgranti*, of various populations that carry an intermediate coloration (bluish-yellow body) could only be an indication that *A. steveni* and *A. stuartgranti* originate from a phylum common only to them. The evolutionary tendencies of these two species are not influenced by this.

This procedure can be explained in more detail as follows: when observing the Tanzanian populations and subjecting them to an analysis of characteristics, it turns out that they reflect the same evolutionary tendencies as the Kande Island population (= *A. steveni*), i.e., they are identical with this population. Conversely formulated: based on the absence of evolutionary differentiation one can thus assume that in contrast to *A. stuartgranti* we are (still) faced with one and the same species, namely with *A. steveni*.

The same holds, by the way, for the yellow Usisya population (to be classified as *A. steveni*) and conversely for the blue population of Nkhata Bay (to be classified as *A. stuartgranti*).

(It must be emphasized that the frequently used biological species concept is completely inadequate when studying populations that do not overlap in their distribution areas (allopatric populations). A meaningful analysis of relationships can only take place on the basis of the evolutionary species concept.)

Naturally, if one believes that color differences should not be employed in the definition of species and only the biological species concept is to be used, a different picture emerges. According to that view, *A. steveni*, *A. stuartgranti*, *A. hueseri*, and *A. korneliae* must all be considered synonyma to *A. baenschi* (and possibly other species as well). *A. baenschi* was the first species described from this group and thus has name priority. This, however, would neglect the phylogenetic development of the various populations from a taxonomic viewpoint, and it is crucial that the system used reflects the phylogenetic lines. In this context, it is irrelevant whether certain populations are formally classified as species, subspecies or races.

**Comments**

The populations of Undu Point and Hai Reef are also exported under the trade names *A.* "Blue Neon" (Lepel 1993a) and *A.* "Blue Dorsal Flavescent" (DeMason 1994a).

Group of *Aulonocara steveni* (Pontoon, Mbamba Bay)

*Aulonocara steveni* (Hai Reef)

57

# *Aulonocara* "Yellow Top"

## Name

The name refers to the broad yellow submarginal band of the dorsal fin which is unusual for representatives of the genus *Aulonocara*. Commercially, this species also occurs under the name of *A.* "Lwanda". Lwanda is the name of a native catcher of ornamental fish.

## Characteristics

Relatively elongated peacock cichlid which reaches a total length of ca 10 to 12 cm. Females monochrome grey to brown with the pattern only hinted at in dark vertical bars. Males with blue head. Shoulder, chest and nape exhibit intensive yellow pigmentation or yellow scale margins. The rear flanks are bluish to dark-blue. The fins, except for the pectoral fins, are also blue. Dorsal and anal fin sport a broad yellow margin. As for individual differences, the caudal fin may also contain yellow pigmentation, particularly in the exterior trailing edges.

## Distribution

This species was observed by us exclusively at Hai Reef near the border of Mozambique. The nearest settlement in Tanzania is Ngombo.

## Habitat and feeding

*A.* "Yellow Top" lives at Hai Reef over a mixed rock-sand bottom at depths ranging from 5 m to at least 15 m. Males are territorial and always linger near rocks or stones. The center of their territory is a crevice or (mostly) a rocky overhang, which functions for rear cover and offers escape. The males patrol frequently in front of their shelter. The size of territory of the males observed by us was roughly 0.5 m in a semicircle. Females were observed alone between rocks. Food was obtained from the bottom or from rocks covered by sediment.

## Similar species

Owing to the somewhat pointed head and the elongated body shape (relatively long for *Aulonocara*) *A.* "Yellow Top" is reminiscent of *A. jacobfreibergi* found by us at Njambe and Hongi Island. In our opinion, *A.* "Yellow Top" is not to be classified as a geographical race of this species (cf. *A.* "Mamelela). With regard to the characteristics described above, *A.* "Yellow Top" and *A.* "Mamelela" appear to be intermediate forms of the other rock-dwelling rather high-backed peacock cichlids.

## Comments

*A.* "Yellow Top" has already been imported frequently.

*Aulonocara* "Yellow Top" (Hai Reef)

*Aulonocara* "Yellow Top", subadult male (Hai Reef)

Representatives of this genus most probably do not form a homogeneous unit. Melanin patterns are partly very variable. The pattern considered the original (plesiomorphic) one, consisting of two longitudinal stripes, as well as the three-spot pattern and largely absent patterns, can be found in the genus *Copadichromis*. One common characteristic of all *Copadichromis* consists in their lifestyle; they all live in more or less open water. Many species live in large shoals during most of the year. The basic food supply is zoo- or phytoplankton which is seized with a pursed mouth. To achieve this the mouth can be turned inside out in a tube-like fashion. This mouth structure is considered an additional feature for the definition of the genus *Copadichromis* (ILES 1960, ECCLES & TREWAVAS 1989: 294–310). Native fishermen of Malawi call *Copadichromis* spp. Utaka and catch them mostly near underwater reefs, using Chirimila nets. It has been known for a long time that large shoals of Utaka frequently hover above submerged reefs sometimes at great depths.

At spawning time, the males retreat to the bottom and create territories, for example, on the surface of rocks. *C. chrysonotus*, however, is known for its spawning in open water (ECCLES & LEWIS 1981). The males of some species seem to occupy territories near the littoral or on rocks for the greater part of the year (e.g., *C. borleyi*).

Overall length is ca 10 to 20 cm; most species reach about 15 cm. Many *Copadichromis* are probably widespread and one should be able to find them on nearly all coasts (for example, *C. chrysonotus*, *C. borleyi*, *C. quadrimaculatus*). At present, 20 species have been described scientifically, and some other species are known under working or trade names. For aquaristic purposes, many species were introduced in the 1980s, but mostly under incorrect names.

As already suggested, from a taxonomical viewpoint the Utaka are a group that still needs much study, not only with respect to the definition of the group or subgroups but also to the individual species. In particular, differentiation vis-à-vis the closely related *Nyassachromis* spp. is often difficult or downright impossible if the current definition of genus is used. The following species follow the classification of ECCLES & TREWAVAS (1989).

*Copadichromis* spp. are able to protrude their mouths to form a "sucking tube" (Liuli).

A school of juvenile *Copadichromis* sp. feeding on plankton (Lundu).

*Copadichromis jacksoni* (Makonde)

# *Copadichromis borleyi* (ILES 1960)

## Characteristics

Medium-sized, moderately high-backed cichlid which reaches a total length of roughly 15 to 17 cm. The pattern consists of three body spots. Females silvery-grey, older individuals sometimes brownish. Males with blue head and usually blue back. The forehead area has a light-blue blaze marked more or less prominently, depending on the individual. The flanks exhibit yellowish or ochre-colored pigmentations or scale margins so that as a whole the body appears to be yellow. In fully colored males, the pattern is submerged and no longer visible. The dorsal fin is blue with broad white margin and white tips. The anal fin is mostly yellow-blue with broad yellow margin. Important for identification are the pelvic fins which in the male are often very elongated.

## Distribution

Probably distributed throughout the entire lake. In Tanzania we found these cichlids at Kirondo, Makonde, Pombo Reef, and in Mbamba Bay.

## Habitat and feeding

*C. borleyi* is usually found in shallow water ranging from 5 m to about 20 m. The preferred habitat appears to consist of large stones or rocks. The males are territorial in the immediate surroundings of rocks in open water and dwell about one to several meters from the bottom. Here the upper surface of the rock forms the center of the territory; but frequently slanting lateral rock faces are also defended. At all four locations, several males lived in one defined area and had established their territory on the neighboring rocks. We frequently observed that the males left their territory to impress or intimidate their neighbors and to re-stake their own territorial borders. These territories, defended in particular against males of the same species, were comparatively large and comprised areas of at least 2 × 2 m. The females lived mostly in small groups of about three to eight individuals above the rocks. *C. borleyi* feeds primarily on plankton.

## Similar species

A number of comparable species exist. In their natural habitat, the males of *C. borleyi* are easily recognized by their life style described above in connection with their coloration and the elongated pelvic fins. A species very similar in coloration is *C. mbenjii* from the group of Mbenji islands off the west coast of the lake. These males essentially display similar coloration and a comparable pattern. *C. mbenjii* males, however, do not sport elongated pelvic fins and in contrast to *C. borleyi* have a yellow, not a blue nape. The females of both species are very hard to distinguish on the basis of head shape. There are several other *Copadichromis* spp. with a three-spot pattern (for example, *C. trimaculatus*). While dominant males can be distinguished with relative ease on the basis of their different coloration, the females are often very similar to each other.

*Copadichromis borleyi* (south of Mbamba Bay)

*Copadichromis borleyi* (Makonde)

63

# *Copadichromis* "Fire Crest Wimpel"

## Name

The trade name for the populations of the eastern Malawi coast reads *C.* "Fire Crest Mloto" (see Comments). This refers to the white blaze (crest) on the forehead and to the red pigmentation (fire) occurring in some populations in the dorsal fin (SPREINAT 1988a).

## Characteristics

Comparatively elongate Utaka, reaching an overall length of about 15 cm. Females are a monochrome grey. Melanin pattern nonexistent or, depending on mood, sometimes with faint dark vertical bars. Dominant males are deep black, with iridescent white forehead and upper back portion. The white coloration runs as a narrow stripe over the back to the upper edge of the caudal peduncle. The dorsal fin is also whitish. The upper and lower edge of the caudal fin is white, with a broad white edge that varies in width according to the individual. Evidently during spawning, the males develop elongated white tips on the caudal fin (German: Wimpel = pennant). Cheek area metallic brownish to greenish. Another feature that deserves mentioning is that the ocelli-like yellow spots in the anal fin look as if they were lined up on the lower edge.

## Distribution

The first population became known on the eastern coast of Malawi north of Makanjila/Fort Maguire, near the river Masinje (Gome Rock). Other populations live in the southwest of the lake at Chinyankhwazi Island (author's observations). In Tanzania we found *C.* "Fire Crest Wimpel" primarily in the northern area of the

Livingstone Mountains. We observed this species relatively often at Nkanda and Makonde. This species probably has a wide distribution throughout the entire lake.

## Habitat and feeding

Intermediate habitats in deep water represent the preferred biotop of *C.* "Fire Crest Wimpel". Depending on location, one can find these cichlids at depths of 20 to 30 m. The maximal depth should be around 50 m. The males are aggressively territorial. On the east coast of Malawi, the author was able to observe how the males had dug out small hollows next to rocks. Contrastingly, the populations found in Tanzania defended larger stones or the surface of rocks against intruders. The size of their territory was difficult to judge, since population density was relatively low. Males were distributed at distances of 5 to 10 m (or more) over the lake bottom. The females lived in open water and were mostly observed singularly, rarely in small groups. *C.* "Fire Crest Wimpel" seems to feed primarily on plankton.

## Similar species

ILES, in 1960, described *C. virginalis* from Nkhata Bay (ILES 1960: 262–264). Regarding the description of coloration, *C.* "Fire Crest Wimpel" might be *C. virginalis*. ILES also reported on two forms of this species which he was able to identify clearly at Nkhata Bay, but not at other locations. Corresponding underwater observations at Nkhata Bay, which also take into consideration concurrent findings on populations from the east coast, are still pending. Thus, we could not make any judgments and the existing trade name was maintained. A very

*Copadichromis* "Fire Crest Wimpel" (Nkanda)

*Copadichromis* "Fire Crest Wimpel" (Nkanda)

similar species is the so-called *C.* "Fire Crest Yellow" (see below). Since both species inhabit the same biotope, we are undoubtedly faced with two independent species.

## Comments

Meanwhile, three "Fire Crest" species have become known. As the first species, from the beginning to about the middle of the 1980s, a cichlid from the east coast of Malawi (Gome Rock) that is very similar with regard to the male's coloration, was exported under the name of "Fire Crest Mloto" (SPREINAT 1985). This population resides in the same biotope on Malawi's east coast as do the "Fire Crest Wimpel" and "Fire Crest Yellow". Other trade names for this cichlid are "Virginalis Blotch" and "Fire Crest Blotch". The latter term is the most suitable one, because this species, in contrast to the other two, exhibits a large-sized body spot (blotch). Another smaller blotch is formed on the caudal peduncle. Furthermore, the "Fire Crest Blotch" is higher-backed than the other two species. Only after 1986 was the second species introduced commercially under the name of "Fire Crest Mloto". Since this species is distinguished by the elongated ends of the caudal fin in the male sex, the term "Wimpel Fire Crest Mloto" was proposed, and analogously for the elongate yellow species, the name "Yellow Fire Crest Mloto" (SPREINAT 1988a). This terminology is adhered to throughout this text with the superfluous addition "Mloto" being dropped. We were not able to spot *C.* "Fire Crest Blotch" in Tanzania.

It is remarkable that all three species live primarily in deep water. It is known from aquarium observations that both *C.* "Fire Crest Blotch" and *C.* "Fire Crest Wimpel" are not assertive species. Oppressed specimens lose their black coloration within days and become silvery-grey. Perhaps the reason for their deep-water existence is the fact that these species cannot compete with the more assertive species living in shallow waters and so they are pushed into the deep water regions where food is scarce. The iridescent white or yellow forehead blazes possibly function as a signal in the ill-lit layers of deep water.

*Copadichromis* "Fire Crest Blotch" (Makanjila/Fort Maguire)

66

*Copadichromis* "Fire Crest Wimpel" (Makanjila/Fort Maguire)

*Copadichromis* "Fire Crest Wimpel", female (aquarium photo)

*Copadichromis* "Fire Crest Blotch" (Makanjila/Fort Maguire)

*Copadichromis* "Fire Crest Blotch", female (Makanjila/Fort Maguire)

*Copadichromis* "Fire Crest Blotch" (Makanjila/Fort Maguire)

# Copadichromis "Fire Crest Yellow"

## Name

This species was first discovered at Malawi's east coast near Makanjila/Fort Maguire (SPREI-NAT 1988a). The working name refers to the yellow blaze and upper back (see also *C.* "Fire Crest Wimpel").

## Characteristics

Medium-sized, elongated species, reaching a total length of ca 12 to 13 cm. Females monochrome grey to silvery without a distinct pattern. Depending on mood, faint, dark vertical bars may occur. Males deep-black with iridescent yellow forehead and nape. The yellow pigmentation continues from the base of the dorsal fin to the upper edge of the caudal fin. In some individuals the dorsal fins are black with broad yellow margin: other specimens exhibit a completely yellow dorsal fin. The tips of the dorsal fin are whitish. The caudal fin is yellow to yellow-black. Conspicuous: the light-blue lower and upper tips of the caudal fin. The ocelli in the anal fin are not as lined up as in *C.* "Fire Crest Wimpel".

## Distribution

Ikombe, Nkanda, Lumbira, and the Bay of Liuli (found in fishermen's nets). Another population lives on Malawi's east coast, north of Makanjila/Fort Maguire (Masinji river, Gome Rock). This species is probably well distributed along the entire east coast.

## Habitat and feeding

Similar to *C.* "Fire Crest Wimpel", this species prefers deep water, usually starting at 20 m. On the east coast of Malawi, the author was able to observe a population between 30 and 40 m. Intermediate habitats seem to be preferred. Males are territorial and defend areas in front of rocks or stones on sand or sometimes the surface of rocks. Distances between males could not be determined because of the relatively low population density. The females showed no interest in the substrate. Like other species of this genus, *C.* "Fire Crest Yellow" seems to feed primarily on plankton.

## Similar species

See *C.* "Fire Crest Wimpel".

*Copadichromis* "Fire Crest Yellow" (Makanjila/Fort Maguire)

*Copadichromis* "Fire Crest Yellow" (Nkanda)

*Copadichromis* "Fire Crest Yellow" (Nkanda)

# Copadichromis "Mloto White Top"

## Name

This cichlid was discovered on the islands of Likoma and Chisumulu and first introduced commercially as "Mloto" and also as "Chrysonotus" (STAECK 1988). It must be emphasized that this species is conspecific neither with *C. mloto* nor with *C. chrysonotus*, which are clearly two different species. Other names are "Mloto White Head", "Mloto Likoma", and "Mloto Ivory".

## Characteristics

Medium-sized, moderately elongate cichlid, reaching an overall length of ca 12 to 13 cm. The pattern consists of three dark body spots. Female silvery-grey. Male with deep-black body coloration. Highlighted in light-blue to white are forehead, the upper back area, and the dorsal fin. The anal fin is black with a white margin. Ocelli are not exhibited or only as stripe-like elements. The caudal fin is black with sometimes a white upper edge.

## Distribution

On the Tanzanian coast, this species is found with relative frequency in the area of Lupingu. In addition, we also found *C.* "Mloto White Top" on the rocky coast between Lupingu and Manda. Two other populations are known from Likoma and Chisumulu.

## Habitat and feeding

*C.* "Mloto White Top" primarily settles on mixed substrates, usually in deep water from about 10 m. At Lupingu, we mainly found these cichlids at about 15 to 20 m. The males were territorial and defended their domain even against heterospecific intruders. The center of their territory was usually a stony crevice or a perpendicular or slanting rock wall, at the base of which we occasionally saw small hollows. Females lived solitary between the male territories. Several times we were able to observe how *C.* "Mloto White Top" picked up food from the bottom. The females also showed a marked interest in the substrate and did not, like so many other Utaka, stay in open water.

## Similar species

The characteristic feature of this species consists of its black body coloration with contrasting white forehead and upper flank regions. Such stark black-and-white or blue-and-white contrast coloration exists in several species in the male sex. In the preceding text the three "Fire Crest" species have already been pointed out. Other species are *C. chrysonotus*, *C. quadrimaculatus*, and *C. cyaneus*, although these three species are primarily blue and not black and clearly grow to a larger size. In the wild, owing to their differing life styles, there is hardly any danger of confusing them.

## Comments

The cited populations from Tanzania differ from the Likoma and Chisumulu populations in their broader white zone in the upper body area.

*C.* "Mloto White Top", because of its preference for bottom-dwelling, should not be considered a typical *Copadichromis*.

*Copadichromis* "Mloto White Top" (Magunga)

*Copadichromis* "Mloto White Top" (north of Lupingu)

# *Copadichromis* cf. *prostoma*

## Name

This cichlid might be conspecific with *C. prostoma*. The type location of *C. prostoma* is Vua at Chilumba. With respect to pattern, body shape and size there is a great similarity (see ECCLES & TREWAVAS 1989: 296–297).

## Characteristics

Small, elongate cichlid. Total length ca 10 to 12 cm. Melanin pattern consists of two dark longitudinal bands, partly interrupted. The first longitudinal band runs from the upper end of the operculum into the caudal peduncle. The second longitudinal band is centered between the first one and the base of the dorsal fin. At the base of the dorsal fin a series of dark spots is occasionally visible. Basic body coloration of dominant males is bluish to blue-black. Black pigmentation is also found in the anal fin and in the lower part of the dorsal fin. The tips of the dorsal fin are yellowish. The caudal fin also exhibits yellow elements. Females are grey to silvery.

## Distribution

We noticed this species along many coastal sections (Ikombe to Hai Reef). Probably widely distributed on the Tanzanian coast. The author found similar populations also on the east coast of Malawi (Makanjila/Fort Maguire).

## Habitat and feeding

*C.* cf. *protoma* prefers the sandy zone. Only rarely did we find this species in intermediate habitats between stones if free sand areas were available. The males are territorial and construct small sand nests. Females live solitary or in small groups over sand. *C.* cf. *prostoma* feeds both on small animals that are adsorbed by the substrate and on plankton. Their preferred depth of water apparently lies between 3 to 15 m. This species is very shy and reacts with instant flight to the exhalation noises of the diver.

## Similar species

Several species of the genus *Nyassachromis* and *C. eucinostomus*, based on their life style in the sandy zone and the slender body form, appear to form one ecological group. The taxonomy of these species is difficult, and it is evident that further undescribed species from this group exist. Few species from this group have been identified reliably in recent times (cf. *Nyassachromis*).

*Copadichromis* cf. *prostoma* (Pombo Reef)

*Copadichromis* cf. *eucinostomus* in front of his sand nest (Likoma)

# Copadichromis "Verduyni Deep Blue"

## Name

The populations introduced here, with respect to life style, body form and coloration, show a strong similarity to *C. verduyni* from Malawi's east coast. It is highly probable that this species is a geographic race of *C. verduyni*.

## Characteristics

Medium-sized cichlid, variable with respect to relative body height. Total length ca 12 to 13 cm. The pattern consists of three dark to black spots on the flanks. The latter are only recognizable in females, but not in males that are in full breeding coloration. Depending on mood, faint, dark vertical bars may also emerge. Females grey to silvery. In the male sex, *C.* "Verduyni Deep Blue" has a very variable coloration, depending on the population. Even within one population there is a certain range of variation. The basic coloration is dark-blue to black. Depending on population, greater or lesser amounts of yellow pigmentation are exhibited on the flanks and in the anal fin. The dorsal fin has a white margin. The populations on the rocky coast south of Kirondo sport a white forehead blaze. For the different colorations in the male see the underwater photographs.

## Distribution

We found this species at Kirondo, Makonde, Lupingu, Magunga, the rocky coast north of Manda, Pombo Reef, Tumbi Reef, Lundu, Puulu, Hongi Island, Lundo Island, and in Mbamba Bay at the pontoon, at the northern rocky coast, Luhuchi Rocks, Mara Rocks, and Ngkuyo Island. The area of distribution thus stretches over a coastal section of roughly 220 km (as the crow flies).

## Habitat and feeding

*C.* "Verduyni Deep Blue" prefers a mixed substrate of shallow water beginning at 5 m and reaching depths of at least 30 m. Males are very territorial and defend territories between or near rocks and stones. Females live mostly in groups of a few specimens above the substrate. In some locations — doubtless in dependence on population density — we were able to observe larger shoals of females, reaching at least 30 specimens (for example, at Luhuchi Rocks, Mbamba Bay). On the rocky coast south of Kirondo, we found a male which at a depth of about 25 m was spawning with a female between rocks. The spawning took place directly on the bottom without the male having made a hollow depression first. As for feeding, we were able to observe several times that both the males and females picked up food from the bottom or from rocks covered by sediment, i.e., unlike the Utaka, they did not feed on plankton. Also, the females showed no tendency whatsoever to move away from the bottom or into open water, but always remained oriented towards the bottom.

## Similar species

As already mentioned under Name, the species under discussion is, in all probability, a geographical race of *C. verduyni*. As early as the beginning of the 1980s this cichlid, coming from the region of Makanjila/Fort Maguire, became known under the trade name "Haplochromis Borleyi Eastern" (SPREINAT 1985). Another form or geographical variant is *C.* "Kawanga" (also known as *C.* "Borleyi Kawanga") from the northwest coast, which, similar to

*Copadichromis* "Verduyni Deep Blue" (north of Kirondo)

*Copadichromis* "Verduyni Deep Blue" (south of Kirondo)

75

C. "Verduyni Deep Blue", is characterized by an overall dark coloration. Another cichlid that might be included among the close relatives of C. verduyni, is C. azureus. This species lives along the middle and southern west coast and can frequently be found at the Mbenji and Maleri group of islands. C. azureus is colored metallic blue all over.

Finally, we must mention the population of C. "Verduyni Northern" which is found north of Kirondo at Ikombe, Nkanda, and Lumbira (see below).

**Comments**

Underwater, C. "Verduyni Deep Blue" is conspicuous not only for its dark coloration, but also for its behavior. In contrast to many other *Copadichromis* this species is by no means shy and is hardly impressed by the underwater photographer.

It is noteworthy that nearly all C. verduyni males that the author observed on the east coast of Malawi had constructed their nests in front of stones. The same behaviour occurs in C. "Kawanga" along the northwest coast. On the northeast coast, however, we observed territorial males with as well as without spawning nests.

*Copadichromis* "Verduyni Deep Blue" (Puulu)

*Copadichromis* "Verduyni Deep Blue" (Mara Rocks, Mbamba Bay)

*Copadichromis* "Verduyni Deep Blue" (Pombo Reef)

*Copadichromis verduyni* (Makanjila/Fort Maguire)

*Copadichromis* "Verduyni Deep Blue", female (Mara Rocks, Mbamba Bay)

*Copadichromis* "Verduyni Deep Blue" (Mbamba Bay, northern rocky coast)

# *Copadichromis* "Verduyni Northern"

### Name

As with the preceding species, we are probably faced with a geographical race of *C. verduyni*. "Northern" refers to the habitat which is located in the extreme north, stretching roughly from Ikombe to Lumbira.

### Characteristics

Medium-sized cichlid with a total length of about 12 cm. Female grey to beige-colored. In contrast to populations occurring south of Lumbira, *C.* "Verduyni Northern" does not exhibit three spots on the flanks but rather only a barely visible pattern of spots. The males sport a blue head and are blue in the upper flank area. The lower flanks exhibit yellow pigmentation, varying in intensity from individual to individual. The dorsal fin has white a margin.

### Distribution

This cichlid is distributed throughout the coastal areas of Ikombe, Nkanda and Lumbira.

### Habitat and feeding

See also *C.* "Verduyni Deep Blue". Intermediate habitats from about 5 m to at least 30 m. The males form territories which lie between or near stones and rocks. Females can be found solitary or in groups of three to five specimens. *C.* "Verduyni Northern" feeds primarily from the bottom or from sediments covering rocks or stones. If available, this species will, of course, also feed on plankton.

### Similar species

See under *C.* "Verduyni Deep Blue". According to our observations, the females — in contrast to the populations living south of Lumbira referred to as "Verduyni Deep Blue" — show no (or only a weakly formed) three-spot pattern. Also, the males are colored a considerably lighter hue. For this reason the populations were defined as separate ones. In a taxonomic framework one could, for example, classify the northern populations as a subspecies.

### Comments

It is noteworthy that in *C.* "Verduyni Northern" a geographical form developed in a coastal section that is not isolated by any obvious barriers (for example, deep water or large sand bay) from the southern coast. In this context, it should be mentioned that this cichlid and also *C.* "Verduyni Deep Blue" exhibit no deep bond with rocky substrates. Thus we were also able to find *C.* "Verduyni Deep Blue" on the sunken pontoon on the sandy bottom at Mbamba Bay. To settle on this artificial reef, the specimens in question would have to travel over wide stretches of sand, since the next rocky coasts are several hundred meters away.

*Copadichromis* "Verduyni Northern" (Lumbira)

*Copadichromis* "Verduyni Northern" (Nkanda)

In the context of the most recent revision of Non-Mbunas (ECCLES & TREWAVAS 1989: 277–281) *E. ornatus, E. lobochilus,* and *E. festivus* were placed in this genus. According to these authors *Eclectochromis* spp. are characterized by a rather primal and comparatively undeveloped pattern, consisting of vertical and horizontal elements. The crucial feature are the strongly developed, pursed lips that bend hooklike upwards and downwards.

The type species of the genus is *E. ornatus,* the description of which is based on only two specimens. The exact location of the type specimens is not known ("Lake Nyasa"). The description of *E. lobochilus* is based on one specimen from Chilumba, likewise for *E. festivus* (type location: Nkhudzi, south of Monkey Bay). All three species are probably identical (see *E. ornatus,* Comments).

Other, scientifically undescribed species which are ordered under this genus, are called *E.* "Hertae" (Likoma, Chisumulu) and *E.* "Thick Lip Mbenji" (Mbenji Islands, middle west cost) (SPREINAT 1989a).

ECCLES & TREWAVAS (1989: 113–115) ordered *E. milomo* under the genus of *Placidochromis.* The deciding factor in this was the pattern, which consists of black vertical bars. However, this is very variable (see below). Furthermore, *E. milomo* has the typical *Eclectochromis* lip form and also resembles the other species in its body shape, while barely showing any similarities to the *Placidochromis* spp. For these reasons it appears better to order this species under the genus of *Eclectochromis.*

*Eclectochromis* spp. settle in rocky, intermediate and partially sandy regions. The pursed lips are considered an adaptation to their way of feeding. One hypothesis states that when grazing the rough rock surfaces, the pursed lips virtually seal off the rock surface and the small animals hidden in crevices are literally sucked out (ECCLES & TREWAVAS 1983: 115). This hypothesis does not explain, however, why the lips are enlarged in a hook-like shape upwards and downwards. Another explanation surmises that these lip extensions contain an greater concentration of sensory cells ("taste cells") which enables the fish to track hidden organisms in the sediment or algal mat (FRYER 1959). That the unusual lip form depends on their feeding habits, is now considered to be an established fact.

It is known that specimens caught over sandy bottoms exhibit no pursed (or only barely pursed) lips. Likewise, aquarium-bred fishes also do not develop pursed (or only barely pursed) lips (SPREINAT 1992b). Clearly, the enlargement of lips is connected with the grazing on rocks.

Another species with enlarged lips is *Cheilochromis euchilus.* This cichlid, however, exhibits a pattern consisting of two distinct longitudinal stripes so that it has been placed in a special (monotypic) genus.

*Eclectochromis* "Hertae" (Likoma Island)

*Eclectochromis* "Labrosus Mbenji" (Mbenji Island)

81

# Eclectochromis milomo  (OLIVER 1989)

## Characteristics

Large cichlid, relatively high-backed; in old age, reaching a total length of about 20 cm. Upper and lower lip are enlarged and hook-like, especially in larger specimens. The pattern, as a rule, consists of broad black cross stripes. In juveniles the cross stripes are irregular. Deviations with respect to the pattern do occur (cf. the photograph of the specimen from Manda). Basic body coloration of females: grey-beige to brownish. Males exhibit a bluish to blue-yellowish flank coloration. The head is usually an intensive blue.

## Distribution

Probably distributed throughout the entire lake. Documented locations range from the south and the southeast arm of the lake up to the Mbenji Islands, Nkhata Bay, and Likoma (ECCLES & TREWAVAS 1989: 115) and Malawi's east coast at Makanjila (SPREINAT 1989a) up to the northeast, where we encountered this species relatively often at Magunga, Cove Mountain, and on the rocky coast north of Manda. Generally speaking this species is, however, rare.

## Habitat and feeding

E. milomo settles on rocky and mixed substrates and is found primarily in deeper water starting at 10 m. As a rule, one encounters single specimens which are not territorial but appear to roam aimlessly across the lake bottom. This species is probably not territorial, not even the male sex, or only slightly so. At the Mbenji Islands, the author found a male in full breeding color and at some distance a female. The male swam in a beeline towards the female and start-ed his courtship. RIBBINK et al. (1983: 247; as Cyrtocara "labrosa") reported that in April of 1980 they were able to observe six territory-defending males at Nakanthenga Island (Maleri Islands) at distances of about 4 m. Based on aquarium observations, males will defend a certain area against all other fishes, at least during the spawning phase.

E. milomo feeds on insect larvae and other small organisms which live in rock-associated algal mats (cf. description of genus).

## Similar species

RIBBINK et al. (1983: 247) listed the population of the Maleri Islands as "Maleri Thick Lip". Specimens from the group of Maleri Islands are distinguished by numerous brownish to ochre-colored pigmentations in the head and flank area, so that these animals have a brownish rather than a white basic coloration.

## Comments

E. milomo became commercially known as "Haplochromis VC 10". VC 10 was a type of airplane used in Malawi. According to EDWARDS (personal communication 1984) who caught this species in the south of the lake, the name is an allusion to the fast swimming style of this species.

*Eclectochromis milomo* (aquarium photo)

*Eclectochromis milomo* (Manda)

*Eclectochromis milomo* (Maleri Island)

83

# *Electochromis ornatus* (REGAN 1922)

## Characteristics

Medium-large, moderately high-backed cichlid that reaches a total length of about 20 cm. Melanin pattern very variable. Larger specimens usually with more or less irregularly crossed stripes and two individual strongly marked longitudinal bands. The midlateral longitudinal band, as a rule, is better defined than the second one which runs approximately centered between the first one and the beginning of the dorsal fin. The longitudinal bands are particularly visible in younger specimens. Furthermore, there is frequently a row of spots at the beginning of the dorsal fin. Specimens from Nkhata Bay usually show an irregular pattern consisting of vertical spots. Basic body coloration of females and juveniles is silvery-grey to brownish. Dominant males sport a greenish cheek and a blue body coloration. The throat and chest area is mostly yellowish-orange. The coloration of males from Tanzania corresponds to that of males from the northwest coast from the Chilumba/Chewere region.

## Distribution

Probably distributed throughout the entire lake. Specimens destined for export from Malawi come overwhelmingly from Malawi's east coast (Makanjila/Fort Maguire) and the Maleri Islands. *E. ornatus* is also frequently found on the northwest coast in the region around Chilumba and the northern bordering coasts. On the Tanzanian coast, we found this cichlid not only in the region of the Livingstone Mountains (Nkanda, Kirondo), but also in the south at Lundo Island and Hai Reef.

## Habitat and feeding

*E. ornatus* prefers mixed substrates in shallow water. Most often one will find this species at depths of about 5 to 15 m. The males form territories between rocks or larger stones. Females live solitary or in small groups. Brooding females release their fry on or between stones and then defend the area. After a short time, the fry are taken back into the mouth and the female swims on. We observed this species when feeding from the bottom and on Aufwuchs. Like *E. milomo*, *E. ornatus* probably feeds primarily on insect larvae and other invertebrates.

## Similar species

With respect to body shape, lip form and coloration, *E.* "Thick Lip Mbenji" and *E.* "Hertae" must be listed as similar species. *E.* "Thick Lip Mbenji", so far only known from the group of Mbenji Islands, can be ordered quite easily owing to the chessboard pattern that is typical for this species. *E.* "Hertae" lives on the coasts of Likoma and Chisumulu and does not exhibit such strongly pursed lips. This latter species is also smaller in most cases and has no greenish cheek area.

## Comments

*E. ornatus* became popular in aquaristic circles under the misleading name of "Haplochromis Flavimanus". At first the author assumed that "Flavimanus" was identical with *E. lobochilus* (SPREINAT 1989a, b). This is indeed true for the population of Chilumba. The only type specimen of *E. lobochilus* comes from Chilumba. Nevertheless, based on our own observations, this species, with respect to the pattern and also

*Eclectochromis ornatus* (Chewere, Chilumba)

*Eclectochromis ornatus* (aquarium photo)

the formation of pursed lips, is so variable that fluid transitions to *E. ornatus* exist. In light of this fact, it does not appear justified to maintain *E. lobochilus* as an autonomous species. As the older species, *E. ornatus* has name priority, so that *E. lobochilus* must be considered synonymous to *E. ornatus*. *E. festivus* should probably also be viewed as being the same species as *E. ornatus*. The only type specimen of this species, an 8.5 cm half-grown fish, comes from the south of the lake (Nkhudzi, south of Monkey Bay). Based on present knowledge no other species lives here but *E. ornatus*. In view of the background of variability of this species, it would seem likely that the slight morphological differences (lower number of gill-rakers, slightly enlarged pharyngeal teeth; ECCLES & TREWAVAS 1989: 279), seen in the only one reference specimen, lie within the range of variation of *E. ornatus*.

*Eclectochromis ornatus,* female (Lundo Island)

*Eclectochromis ornatus,* territorial male at Makanjila/Fort Maguire

# The genera *Lethrinops* & *Taeniolethrinops* R<small>EGAN</small> 1922

Until recently, a group of cichlids which is distinguished from other "Haplochromis" resp. Non-Mbunas by its feeding habits (sifting of sand for edibles) and its different type of teeth, was summarized under the genus *Lethrinops*. In the most recent revision (E<small>CCLES</small> & T<small>REWAVAS</small> 1989), the *Lethrinops* species were placed in separate genera which either exhibited a diagonal band as a melanin pattern (now called *Taeniolethrinops*) or are distinguished by a special form of the pharynx bone (now called *Tramitichromis*).

The taxonomy of the entire group badly needs revising. E<small>CCLES</small> & T<small>REWAVAS</small> strongly emphasized that there are still several undescribed species and that in a comprehensive revision possibly some synonymization will become necessary. Only for a few species has

actual species membership been sufficiently clarified.

The representatives of this group usually attain a total length of 10 to 20 cm and live above sandy or mixed substrates. The type of feeding is characteristic. Sand (even gravel) is picked up by mouth in portions and sifted for edibles. Some species literally hurtle themselves head over heels into the bottom and disappear up to their eyes (and deeper) into the sand. At least during spawning, males are territorial and construct large sand hollows or even castles.

We found a number of *Lethrinops* representatives in Tanzania. In the following, only those species are described that we were able to observe frequently.

A male *Taeniolethrinops* "Black Fin" stands guard over his sand nest (Lupingu). The small hollows in the lake bottom around the nest are testimony to the digging activity of this species.

# Lethrinops "Yellow Collar"

## Name

The tentative working name of this scientifically still undescribed species goes back to Ribbink et al. (1983: 245), who first mentioned this cichlid in the literature. These authors, however, classified this species as *Aulonocara*. This species, however, does not exhibit greatly enlarged openings of the lateral line system in the head area typical of this genus (cf. *Aulonocara*) and on the basis of teeth must be ordered into the genus *Lethrinops*. Another term, which in recent times was propagated quite unnecessarily, is *Lethrinops* "Nyassae" (Konings 1992: 319).

## Characteristics

Small cichlid, with maximum length of ca 10 cm. Rarely any melanin pattern; depending on mood, faint narrow bars are visible. Females are a monochrome silver to grey. Males are characterized by a blue head (in front) and yellow nape and anterior back area. Another characteristic is the black pigment band formed especially in the rear part of the dorsal fin. In some specimens, the upper part of the caudal fin is also blackish. Another noteworthy feature are the numerous and very large egg spots in the anal fin of the males.

## Distribution

Probably lake-wide distribution. Documented locations lie in the south (region of Monkey Bay, Thumbi West Island) and at Likoma Island (Ribbink et al. 1983: 245). Based on our own observations, it is also present on Malawi's east coast (Makanjila/Fort Maguire) and northwest coast at Chilumba. In Tanzania, we found this cichlid at Lupingu, Lundo Island, and at the northern edge of Mbamba Bay.

## Habitat and feeding

*L.* "Yellow Collar" primarily inhabits the sandy zone. We encountered this cichlid mostly near rocks on the sandy bottom or above sandy regions in deep water at the edge of the rocky habitats. Males are territorial and defend their domain. The center of their territory is usually a depression, whose size evidently depends on population density. The more males existing in a given area, the smaller the depressions appear to be. Females can usually be found in groups on the adjacent sandy bottom. The depth at which this species lives evidently depends on the type of substrate. At some locations, where the rock tapers into sandy areas as early as 10 m, *L.* "Yellow Collar" lives in comparatively shallow water. As a rule, however, this cichlid seems to appear more frequently in deeper water beginning at about 20 m. At Likoma, the author was able to observe this species at 50 m (at the island of Masimbwe), where about 100 fishes lived in one large spawning colony. According to aquarium observations, *L.* "Yellow Collar" is not very assertive and is easily oppressed by other species. It is possible that the life style in deep water is due to the fact that this species is unable to handle the competition for territory in shallow water. *L.* "Yellow Collar" obtains food particles from the substrate by digging in the manner that is typical for *Lethrinops*.

*Lethrinops* "Yellow Collar" (north of Mbamba Bay)

*Lethrinops* "Yellow Collar", female (north of Mbamba Bay)

89

# *Taeniolethrinops* "Black Fin"

## Name

The name refers to the strongly marked black pigmentation in the posterior part of the dorsal of dominant males. It is possible that we are dealing with a species already described (cf. text on genus). Since the entire group is in need of revision, we will not attempt here to order this species into a similar, already described species.

## Characteristics

Medium-large, moderately high-backed cichlid. Total length about 15 cm. Melanin pattern consists of a partly interrupted diagonal stripe, which in the middle is thickened in blotches. In some females, this pattern is only weakly formed. Basic color of females silvery-grey to yellowish. Dominant males exhibit a metallic blue on front of head and in cheek area. Flanks are greenish to yellowish with blue sheen. Lower chest area yellowish. Rear part of dorsal fin and lower part of anal fin are deep-black. Anal fin with strongly marked yellow spots or numerous elongated pigment bands.

## Distribution

This species seems to be distributed over the entire Tanzanian coast. We found *T.* "Black Fin" at Ikombe, Nkanda, Lupingu, Pombo Reef, and Undu Point. On the east coast of Malawi (Makanjila/Fort Maguire), the author was able to observe similar populations.

## Habitat and feeding

Mixed and sandy substrates ranging from shallow water (2–3 m) to a depth of 15 m appear to be the preferred biotopes of this species. The males are strictly territorial and erect crater-like sand nests into which the females are lured for spawning. Directly before Lupingu, we observed several males, which at a depth of about 3 m directly adjacent to a bed of Vallisneria and a rocky region, had erected raised sand nests. The inner diameter of these sand nests was about 60 to 80 cm, the height of the crater's rim about 10 to 20 cm. It was noteworthy that the males piled sand onto the edge not only from the inside but also from the outer side of the nest. In this way a more or less regular, ring-like moat was formed around the nest, with a total diameter of about 1.5 m. This was considered the inner zone of the territory, i.e., no other fish was tolerated within this area. Same-species males were attacked and chased away even before approaching the outer ring. *T.* "Black Fin" obtains food by sifting the substrate portionwise. Small hollows in the substrate are testimony to this type of digging activity.

## Similar species

A species that is similar in body shape is *Lethrinops furcifer.*

*Taeniolethrinops* "Black Fin"
(Lupingu)

*Taeniolethrinops* "Black Fin"
(Pombo Reef)

*Taeniolethrinops* "Black Fin",
subdominant male (Pombo Reef)

91

# *Taeniolethrinops praeorbitalis* (REGAN 1922)

## Characteristics

Large cichlid, which can reach a total length of 25 to 30 cm. A typical feature is the slightly extended, broad snout, giving its mouth a shovel-like appearance. Melanin pattern consists of a dark diagonal stripe, which, however, may disappear completely, depending on mood. Occasionally narrow, faint vertical bars are also visible. Also mood-dependent in some specimens is a forked diagonal stripe which has the form of a "Y" lying on its side. The band of the "Y" pointing obliquely toward the pectoral fin is quite short. The basic body coloration of juveniles, females and subadult males is silvery-grey to yellowish. In particular, the snout and lower head area as well as the chest are of an intensive yellow in some individuals. The yellow coloration frequently extends to the pelvic and anal fins. Dominant males do not show yellow coloration, but are dark-greenish to bluish all over.

## Distribution

This species probably has a lake-wide distribution. According to ECCLES & TREWAVAS (1989: 261), *T. praeorbitalis* frequently occurs in the south of the lake and also at Mbenji Island. Based on our own observations, this cichlid also lives along Malawi's east coast (Makanjila/Fort Maguire) as well as along the northwest coast (Chilumba). In Tanzania, we found *T. praeorbitalis* at Lupingu and Cove Mountain.

## Habitat and feeding

*T. praeorbitalis* is an inhabitant of the sandy zone, ranging from shallow water to depths of more than 50 m (ECCLES & TREWAVAS 1989: 261;

30 fathoms = ca 55 m). This species is encountered solitary or in small troops of two to four specimens. During spawning the males occupy territories (KONINGS 1992: 322).

*T. praeorbitalis* feeds primarily on insect larvae (ECCLES & TREWAVAS 1983: 261), which are "dug out" from the substrate. To this end the fish plunges vertically into the substrate occasionally even disappearing up to its eyes. Its mouth filled with sand; it reemerges and sifts the sand for edibles. Fine particles are discarded through the gill slits. This burrowing activity attracts other fish which snap up disturbed bottom-dwelling organisms. Some species, as for example, *Cyrtocara moorii*, follow *T. praeorbitalis* over long distances, thus forming a feeding community of sorts.

## Similar species

The elongated snout in connection with the diagonal stripe is typical, thus making this species relatively easy to recognize.

## Comments

Despite its size, *T. praeorbitalis* is peaceful in the aquarium and is easily socialized with other, much smaller species. *T. praeorbitalis* develops a colossal appetite. This species has already been bred in aquariums.

*Taeniolethrinops praeorbitalis* (aquarium photo)

*Taeniolethrinops praeorbitalis* (aquarium photo)

*Taeniolethrinops praeorbitalis* followed by *Cyrtocara moorii* (Lupingu)

*Taeniolethrinops praeorbitalis* burrowing in the sand (Lupingu)

93

# The genus *Lichnochromis*

TREWAVAS 1935

The genus *Lichnochromis* contains only one species: *L. acuticeps*. The long, laterally strongly compressed snout in connection with a diagonal stripe are the typical characteristics of this genus.

# *Lichnochromis acuticeps*

TREWAVAS 1935

## Characteristics

Medium-large, moderately elongated cichlid with long, laterally very compressed snout. Total length ca 20 to 25 cm. Melanin pattern consists of a dark diagonal band. Basic body coloration of females is silvery-grey to yellowish-brown. Dominant males show a completely green-blue coloration with golden scale edges on the flanks. In some specimens the chest and belly area is yellowish.

## Distribution

*L. acuticeps* has been found at many coastal sections (Monkey Bay, Malawi's east coast at Makanjila/Fort Maguire, Maleri Islands, northwest coast) so that lake-wide distribution can be assumed. This cichlid is relatively frequent along the northwest coast in the region of Nkhata Bay to Chilumba (author's observations). In Tanzania, we spotted this species at Lupingu and Puulu Island. *L. acuticeps* is rare.

## Habitat and feeding

*L. acuticeps* inhabits mixed substrates and is encountered mostly in shallow water down to depths of 15 m. This species is solitary and not territorial. From aquarium observations, it is known that dominant males, especially during courtship and spawning, defend certain areas against all other tank inhabitants. In his natural habitat, *L. acuticeps* is conspicuous — aside from his elongated snout — by his manner of feeding. He purposely swims towards boulders forming a horizontal crevice with the lake bottom. Shortly before reaching this gap, the fish flops over 90 degrees on to its side so as to insert his laterally compressed snout as deeply as possible into the gap. The particles thus picked up are then sifted for food. Evidently the fish cannot see whether and what kind of small organisms are contained in the gap; the mere shape of the gap appears to trigger the feeding behavior (SPREINAT 1992b). In the aquarium one can also observe that this species, particularly after feeding, searches the tank bottom for leftovers. *L. acuticeps* is not a predator. In an aquarium this cichlid can be raised together with much smaller species or with juveniles.

## Similar species

With respect to body shape as well as to melanin pattern, *Mylochromis* cf. *lateristriga* (trade name: "Flame Oxyrhynchus"), *M.* "Pointed Nose" and *M.* "Pointed Nose Tanzania" (see below) are similar. All three species, however, lack the laterally compressed snout. In Tanzania, we found another species (*Mylochromis*

"Mchuse", see below), which also exhibits a long, but not laterally compressed snout.

**Comments**

Aquarium-raised specimens of *L. acuticeps* do not exhibit a snout as strongly compressed laterally as that found in wild-caught fish. This feature probably evolves with the same dependence on feeding as do the pursed lips in *Eclectrochromis ornatus*, *E. milomo*, and *Cheilochromis euchilus* (SPREINAT 1992b).

*Lichnochromis acuticeps* (aquarium photo)

*Lichnochromis acuticeps,* female (Lupingu)

*Lichnochromis acuticeps* during feeding

# The genus *Mylochromis* REGAN 1920

This genus consists of species that are distinguished by a dark diagonal band and which appear relatively unspecialized as morphologically special features are absent. This is in contrast to cichlids that also exhibit a diagonal band but are characterized by other features as well and are thus placed in separate genera (for example, *Buccochromis*: diagonal band + large mouth + predatory lifestyle; *Lichnochromis*: diagonal band + laterally compressed snout).

Among the patterns of Lake Malawi cichlids the diagonal band patterns must be especially emphasized. No other cichlid outside Lake Malawi has developed such diagonal band patterns. ECCLES & TREWAVAS (1989: 28) point out that all genera with diagonal bands can probably be traced to their own "lineage" in the genetic tree of Lake Malawi cichlids.

*Mylochromis* representatives usually grow to a size of 15 to 20 cm and are among the non-predatory species. Many species are probably widely distributed.

Note: in the revision of ECCLES & TREWAVAS the genus *Maravichromis* was established for representatives of this genus. Here the authors overlooked the fact that REGAN had in 1920 already introduced the genus *Mylochromis* for *M. lateristriga* (REGAN 1920), which had meanwhile been declared invalid. Thus, a generic name already existed for species with a diagonal band pattern: *Maravichromis* had to be rejected as a junior synonym for *Mylochromis* (DERIJST & SNOEKS 1992).

*Mylochromis lateristriga* (aquarium photo)

Stony zone at about a depth of 10 m (Kirondo).

On expedition with the "Nyanja"; diving site in a small bay about 500 m north of Lupingu.

# *Mylochromis labidodon* (TREWAVAS 1935)

### Characteristics

Medium-large, moderately elongated cichlid. Total length usually ca 15 cm, rarely up to 20 cm. Melanin pattern consists of a diagonal band which may dissolve into a row of spots. These spots are sometimes elongated in a vertical direction so that a pattern of bars may also appear. Basic body color grey to beige. Dominant males show a blue to green head. The scale edges on the flanks are yellow to orange, so that the flanks may appear yellow. The throat and chest area is covered with yellow pigmentation that vary individually. Particularly in older individuals, the concave "saddle-like" profil of the forehead is prominent. Another specialization is the teeth of the lower jaw: the front teeth are considerably larger than the teeth in the subsequent rows.

### Distribution

Probably widely distributed species. Documented locations are at Mwaya (north end of lake) and Chilumba (ECCLES & TREWAVAS 1989: 210). KONINGS reported on occurrences in Lake Malombe (1992: 160). The author observed this species in the south at Tsano Rock (Monkey Bay). In Tanzania, we found *M. labidodon* at Lupingu, Pombo Reef, Lundu, Mbamba Bay (Luhuchi Rocks), and at Hai Reef.

### Habitat and feeding

*M. labidodon* prefers mixed and sandy regions ranging from shallow water to depths of about 15 m. Rarely found at greater depths. Young and subadult *M. labidodon* (total length about 7 to 9 cm) were frequently found in small troops of three to eight individuals. In contrast, sexually mature males and females, were found to be solitary. In each case we were able to establish that this species is not territorial and seemingly roams aimlessly through the underwater scenery. So far, it is not known whether males occupy a territory during spawning. In the wild, *M. labidodon* is conspicuous for its special method of foraging. *M. labidodon* is a "pebble turner", which very forcefully swims towards small stones or pebbles protruding from the substrate and turns them over with his mouth. Following that, the fish paddles backwards, using his pectorals, and checks, head downward, to see what edibles might be waiting beneath the stone. This behavior was observed by us quite frequently in juveniles.

### Similar species

The relatively elongated body in connection with the saddle-like forehead distinguishes this species from previously known *Mylochromis* species. A correspondingly elongated body shape is also exhibited by *M. ericotaenia*.

### Comments

It is remarkable how variable this species can be with respect to its melanin pattern. In some older males the diagonal band is dissolved into vertical spots, thus almost producing a pattern of vertical bars.

*Mylochromis labidodon* (Pombo Reef)

*Mylochromis labidodon*, female (Lundu)

*Mylochromis labidodon* (aquarium photo)

*Mylochromis labidodon* (Tsano Rock,
Monkey Bay)

*Mylochromis labidodon* turning over a pebble
(Luhuchi Rocks, Mbamba Bay)

# *Mylochromis* "Mchuse"

## Name

"Mchuse" was the name of the native catcher, after whom this species has been tentatively named. This cichlid was first shown in a photograph by STAECK (1976: 441) as a possible *Lethrinops* species. DEMASON recently reported on the same species, calling it "Thick Lips Lichnochromis" (DEMASON 1994a).

## Characteristics

Medium-large, moderately elongate cichlid. Total length about 16 to 18 cm. Melanin pattern consists of a solid diagonal band, rarely interrupted in a few spots. Trace of bar pattern. Basic body coloration silvery-grey to faded yellow. Pointed snout with strongly developed lips. Upper lip slightly protruding. The mouth, like that of *Lichnochromis acuticeps*, appears to be slightly beak-shaped, but instead of being compressed laterally it is relatively broad-shaped. Dominant males show different shades of blue, ranging from light to dark-blue. Chest area frequently yellowish. In the unpaired fins, particularly in the caudal fin, the males sport numerous yellow-to-orange pigment stripes.

## Distribution

Evidently widely distributed along the coast of Tanzania, but nothing is known about this species in Malawi. We found *M.* "Mchuse" at Ikombe, Nkanda, Lumbira, Kirondo, Makonde, Lupingu, and Magunga. DEMASON (1994a) reported on a population north of Njambe.

## Habitat and feeding

*M.* "Mchuse" predominantly inhabits mixed substrates. We observed these cichlids most often at a depth between 5 and 10 m. *M.* "Mchuse" is relatively rare. All specimens observed were solitary and not territorial. Underwater, we did not encounter males in breeding coloration, so that no statements can be made about possible territorial behavior. According to our observations, *M.* "Mchuse" feeds primarily on bottom-dwelling invertebrates. With its mouth wide open, this species attacks the sandy or pebbly substrate and sifts it for food.

## Similar species

At first glance *M.* "Mchuse" resembles *Lichnochromis acuticeps*, a species that also sports a long snout and a beak-like mouth. However, in contrast to *L. acuticeps* the snout of *M.* "Mchuse" is not laterally compressed. It is also obvious that *M.* "Mchuse" does not represent a geographical variant of *L. acuticeps*, since the latter species is also encountered on the northeast coast in the same biotopes (see above).

*Mylochromis* "Mchuse" (Lupingu)

*Mylochromis* "Mchuse" (Lupingu)

*Mylochromis* "Mchuse" (Lupingu)

*Mylochromis* "Mchuse", female (Magunga)

*Mylochromis* "Mchuse", female (Makonde)

# *Mylochromis mola*

## Characteristics

Medium-sized species that is relatively high-backed in old age. Total length ca 15 to 18 cm. The melanin pattern consists of genus-typical diagonal band, which, however, is frequently dissolved into a row of spots. Basic coloration silvery-grey to beige. Dominant males are bluish to greenish, particularly in the head area. In some specimens the chest and belly area are yellow.

## Distribution

Very probably *M. mola* has lake-wide distribution. Documented locations are on the northwest coast and in the southeastern and southwestern arms of the lake (ECCLES & TREWAVAS 1989: 222). Based on our own observations this species also lives on Malawi's east coast (Makanjila/Fort Maguire), at the islands of Mbenji, Likoma, and Chisumulu as well as on the northwest coast at Nkhata Bay. In Tanzania, we found this species at Ikombe, Kirondo, Lupingu, Undu Point, and Hai Reef.

## Habitat and feeding

Mixed, primarily sandy zones and *Vallisneria* beds are among the preferred biotopes of *M. mola*. Normally one will find this species in shallow water from a few meters down to 10 to 15 m. Males are mostly aggressively territorial. Some males had constructed sand nests in their territory. Females and subadults live solitary or in groups, which, as a rule, comprise three to ten animals. *M. mola* is considered an eater of molluscs (snails and shells; FRYER & ILES 1972: 272) which are crushed with the aid of its robust pharyngeal teeth.

## Similar species

In principle, a number of similar species of this genus exists, such as *M. mollis, M. incola,* or *M. plagiotaenia.* In contrast to these species, *M. mola* is distinguished by the fact that the diagonal band is more or less dissolved into a row of spots.

## Comments

Despite the large distribution area the males, with respect to their coloration, appear relatively uniform in the context of variational range. From aquarium observations, it is known that this species is peaceful and is easily socialized with other species.

*Mylochromis mola* (Kirondo)

*Mylochromis mola* (Thumbi West Island, Cape Maclear)

*Mylochromis mola*, female (Hai Reef)

*Mylochromis mola* (Lupingu)

*Mylochromis mola* (Ikombe)

*Mylochromis mola* (aquarium photo)

103

# *Mylochromis* "Pointed Head Tanzania"

## Name

The name refers to the pointed shape of the head of this species. Another, possibly conspecific population is known from Malawi's east coast as *M.* "Pointed Head" or also as "Makanjila Mola" (see below).

## Characteristics

Medium-sized, moderately elongate cichlid. Total length mostly ca 12 to 15 cm. A conspicuous feature is the pointed snout (distance between point of mouth and eye) which is also quite long in relation to head length. Melanin pattern consists of a diagonal band, which is solid as a rule. Faded cross bars may be visible, depending on mood. Basic coloration of females is grey to brownish. Dominant males become completely blue with yellow throat and chest area. Unpaired fins sport conspicuous yellow pigment stripes.

## Distribution

We found this species chiefly on the southern coast of Tanzania: Njambe, Mbamba Bay (Luhuchi Rocks), Undu Point, and Hai Reef. Based on author's observations, very similar populations live at Likoma and Nkhata Bay. Possibly a widespread species.

## Habitat and feeding

Primarily mixed substrates in shallow water down to about 20 m depth form the biotopes of this cichlid. Females were observed to be solitary. The males are territorial and defend their domain between the rocks. According to our observations, *M.* "Pointed Head Tanzania" picks up food from the substrate and rock surfaces covered by sediment. Some specimens sifted the substrate for food. The small mouth suggests that this cichlid feeds on small animals.

## Similar species

As already mentioned under Name, a very similar population that probably belongs to the same species exists on Malawi's east coast in the region of Makanjila/Fort Maguire. Specimens of this population have been exported under the names of "Pointed Head" (also "Pointed Nose") and "Makanjila Mola" (SPREINAT 1985). Recently, the name "Lateristriga Makanjila" was added as yet another term to the name confusion game (KONINGS 1992: 164).

Similar, but certainly not conspecific forms have become known from Malawi (for example, *M.* "New Golden Mola" from the Maleri Islands or *M.* "Magrettae Stripe" from Likoma). Of the scientifically already described species, one should mention *M. incola*, *M. mollis,* and *M. lateristriga*. The latter species grows much larger than the others and is known under the trade name of "Flame Oxyrhynchus". The relationships between the various forms/species have not yet been sufficiently clarified.

## Comments

At Undu Point and Luhuchi Rocks (Mbamba Bay), we observed specimens which exhibited a relatively short snout and a continuous diagonal band which, however, did not stretch all the way to the base of the dorsal fin. In view of the high degree of variability in many species with respect to pattern, too few specimens have been found to enable us to judge with certainty whether these individuals represent another species or not.

Because of the abruptly ending diagonal stripe we called these specimens during our field studies *M.* "Stop Line".

*Mylochromis* "Pointed Head Tanzania", female (Hai Reef)

*Mylochromis* "Pointed Head Tanzania" (Hai Reef)

*Mylochromis* cf. "Pointed Head Tanzania" (Undu Point)

105

# *Mylochromis semipalatus* (TREWAVAS 1935)

## Characteristics

Medium-sized, relatively high-backed cichlid. Total length usually ca 15 to 20 cm, rarely larger. Distinct, continuous black diagonal stripe. Basic color mostly yellow. Frequently yellow pigmentation is especially distinct in head, chest and lower flank area. The fins also contain yellow. As a tendency, the yellow coloration is more distinct in younger specimens while fully mature specimens barely exhibit it at all. Dominant males show a blue to green sheen in the head area, which is less pronounced on the flanks.

## Distribution

Probably widely distributed in the entire lake, but nowhere frequently encountered. The type specimens of this species stem from the northwest coast (Chilumba/Kaporo; ECCLES & TREWAVAS 1989: 218). Based on our observations, it is also found on Malawi's east coast (Makanjila/Fort Maguire), in the southeastern part of the lake (Eccles Reef), and on the middle west coast (Senga Bay). In Tanzania, we found this species at Lupingu, Pombo Reef, and Tumbi Reef.

## Habitat and feeding

Sandy or mixed substrates appear to be the preferred biotope of *M. semipalatus*. We found this species solitary, sometimes in small groups. *M. semipalatus* is nowhere frequent, thus our observation pertains to only a few specimens. None of the specimens encountered was territorial. We were unable to observe feeding.

## Similar species

A very similar species with respect to body shape and coloration is *Platygnathochromis*

*melanonotus*. This cichlid exhibits an extremely flat lower jaw. On the basis of this peculiar lower jaw, this species was placed in a genus of its own. Except for the lower jaw, *M. semipalatus* and *P. melanonotus*, as known so far, are identical in every respect. This led to speculations that only one species is concerned, and that the flattened lower jaw, in analogy to the pursed lips of the *Eclectrochromis* spp., can be traced to their special feeding mechanisms (KONINGS 1993). This, however, is strongly contradicted by aquarium observations. While in captive-bred fishes the pursed lips are no longer or only weakly developed because of the absence of their species-typical feeding style, aquarium-raised *P. melanonotus*, raised to sexual maturity on the usual substitute foods, still exhibits the flattened lower jaw throughout its development.

## Comments

*M. semipalatus* and *P. melanonotus* were originally introduced under the trade name of "Haplochromis Yellow Black Line".

*Mylochromis semipalatus,* male and female (Lupingu)

*Mylochromis semipalatus* (aquarium photo)

*Mylochromis semipalatus,* female (Tumbi Reef)

*Mylochromis semipalatus,* female (Malawi)

*Platygnathochromis melanonotus* (Malawi)

107

In this genus, one finds small to medium-sized cichlids with small head and long caudal peduncle and mostly elongate body. Markings do not exist or only in the form of longitudinal or faint bar patterns. Several *Nyassachromis* spp. are sand-dwelling cichlids. In some cases the boundary to the genus *Copadichromis* is uncertain so that a new definition of both genera is desirable.

Presently six *Nyassachromis* spp. have been described formally and scientifically (*N. brevi-* *ceps, N. leuciscus, N. microcephalus, N. nigritaeniatus, N. purpurans, N. serenus*). Identification of the species described, i.e., the classification of populations living in the lake within the already described species is very difficult. Furthermore, in all probability, several as yet undescribed species exist.

In Tanzania there are at least four species that we found in the catch of native fishermen as well as under water. We introduce the most conspicuous species in the following.

# *Nyassachromis* "Yellow Head"

### Name

The name refers to the conspicuous yellow coloring of the forehead. The classification as *Nyassachromis* spp. is based on the absence of a melanin pattern, the slender body and the lifestyle above a sandy substrate.

### Characteristics

Small to medium-sized, elongated cichlid. Total length ca 10 to 12 cm. Melanin pattern nonexistent or consisting of only faintly visible dark vertical bars. Females are a monochrome dark-grey to brownish. Dominant males as a whole are black with brilliant yellow forehead and neck area. Tips of the dorsal and leading edges of the pelvic fins are white. At the leading edge of the anal fin a few large, brilliant yellow spots (egg spots) are formed.

### Distribution

We found this cichlid at Nkanda and Lumbira. Rare species. No species colored like this has become known in Malawi.

### Habitat and feeding

*N.* "Yellow Head" seems to prefer sandy and rarely mixed substrates. Females were found to be solitary and showed no close bond with the substrate. The males constructed shallow sand nests for spawning which were defended against all other fish. We could only find this species in deep water of about 18 to 30 m.

### Similar species

Due to its yellow forehead *N.* "Yellow Head" is reminiscent of *Copadichromis* "Fire Crest Yellow", which otherwise, however, shows a completely different coloration. The formation of a white or yellow forehead seems to indicate a signal function, especially for species living in deep water. Here one must keep in mind that the yellow color components of light are almost completely absorbed at depths of 10 m. This means that at depths of 20 to 30 m the color yellow can no longer be perceived without artificial light (the photographs were taken with an electron flash camera). It is possible that the moving light-dark contrast alone fulfills a signal function.

*Nyassachromis* "Yellow Head" (Lumbira)

One of the two Tanzanian ferry boats, the "Songea" at anchorage in Liuli.

# The genus *Otopharynx*

Relatively non-specialized species with three body spots are summarized in this genus. The first body spot of the so-called three-spot pattern usually lies posterior to the end of the pectoral fins or directly beneath the upper lateral line (supra-pectoral spot). The second spot, as a rule somewhat smaller, is located above the anal fin, roughly between the two lateral lines (supra-anal spot). The third and smallest spot finally is the caudal peduncle spot. As for size and shape, these spots vary considerably even within the same species, but their relative location is usually constant. At present, the genus *Otopharynx* comprises 12 described species. Most species attain total lengths of 15 to 20 cm.

## *Otopharynx* "Big Spot Tanzania"

### Name

The name refers to the first body spot, which is quite large, particularly in northern populations.

### Characteristics

Medium-sized, relatively high-backed cichlid, reaching a total length of ca 14 to 16 cm. Genus-typical three-spot melanin pattern. Basic coloration grey-brown to beige. Dominant males show an intensely blue head and in particular, a blue anterior back. Flanks with individually strongly differing quantities of yellow. Throat and chest area frequently yellow. Dorsal fin with white-yellow edge. Numerous yellow pigment stripes are often formed in the caudal and anal fin.

### Distribution

Probably widely distributed on the Tanzanian coast. We found this cichlid at Lumbira, Kirondo, Lupingu, Magunga, Undu Point, and Hai Reef. Similar populations are known from the coast of Malawi (see Similar species).

### Habitat and feeding

*O.* "Big Spot Tanzania" prefers intermediate habitats at depths of 5 to 15 m. Sometimes we also found this species in a purely rocky zone. Females and subadults live solitary or in small groups. Males in breeding coloration are aggressively territorial. *O.* "Big Spot Tanzania" appear to feed chiefly on invertebrates that occur on the substrate or in the sediment layers on rocky substrates. Not a predatory species. *O.*

*Otopharynx* "Big Spot Tanzania" (Kirondo)

*Otopharynx* "Big Spot Tanzania", female (Magunga)

*Otopharynx* "Big Spot Tanzania" (Lupingu)

*Otopharynx* "Big Spot Tanzania", female (Hai Reef)

*Otopharynx* "Big Spot Tanzania" (Hai Reef)

111

"Big Spot Tanzania" is by no means shy but a curious cichlid.

**Similar species**

From the Island of Likoma, since the beginning of the 1980s, a cichlid has been known under the trade name of "Haplochromis Royal Blue" which shows great similarities in particular to the populations of Undu Point and Hai Reef. Other populations that show similarities to *O.* "Big Spot Tanzania" with respect to body shape, melanin pattern, and to the coloration of dominant males, were found by the author at

Chilumba and at the Maleri Islands (these populations are illustrated as *O.* cf. *heterodon*). It is possible that all of these populations could be classified as geographical forms of a widely distributed species.

The only species described with whom *C.* "Big Spot Tanzania" might be identical is *O. heterodon.* According to data by ECCLES & TREWAVAS (1989: 158) this cichlid is distributed at Chilumba, Monkey Bay, Likoma, and Nkhata Bay. Appropriate comparative investigations with reference to type specimens of this species have not been carried out so far.

Beach of Magunga, a small village south of Cape Kaiser.

*Otopharynx* "Royal Blue" (Chisumulu Island)

*Otopharynx* cf. *heterodon,* female (Chitendi Island, Chilumba)

*Otopharynx* cf. *heterodon* (Chitendi Island, Chilumba)

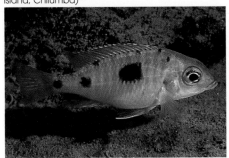

*Otopharynx* cf. *heterodon,* female (Maleri Island)

*Otopharynx* cf. *heterodon* (Maleri Island)

113

# *Otopharynx* "Blue Yellow Tanzania"

## Name

The name refers to the flank coloration of dominant males (Yellow-Blue Otopharynx, SPREINAT 1993a).

## Characteristics

Medium-sized, moderately high-backed cichlid. Total length about 12 to 15 cm. The pointed head is noteworthy. Genus-typical three-spot melanin pattern. Females silvery-grey to beige, sometimes a faint yellow. Dominant males show a blue head and yellow-blue body. Chest and belly are colored yellow. The posteriors of the dorsal and caudal fins contain yellow pigment stripes.

## Distribution

We were able to find this cichlid at Njambe, Hongi Island, and Lundo Island. Possibly wider distribution. No comparable population is known from Malawi so far.

## Habitat and feeding

*O.* "Blue Yellow Tanzania" lives primarily in mixed zones. We encountered this species at depths of about 5 to 15 m. Males are strictly territorial and even defend their territory against other species. The center of the territory might be a rock wall or an overhang. We observed solitary females roaming through the littoral. Food is obtained from the substrate or from the sediment layer deposited on stones and rocks.

## Comments

The pointed head in connection with the three-spot pattern seems unusual. A pointed head shape, together with comparable body shape, is also known for *Mylochromis* spp. Perhaps this is the reason that this cichlid has occasionally been traded under the confusing name of "*Maravichromis* (= *Mylochromis*) Three Spot".

*Otopharynx* "Blue Yellow Tanzania" (Lundo Island)

*Otopharynx* "Blue Yellow Tanzania", female (Hongi Island)

*Otopharynx* "Blue Yellow Tanzania" (Njambe)

*Otopharynx* "Blue Yellow Tanzania" (aquarium photo)

# The genus *Placidochromis*

ECCLES & TREWAVAS 1989

Species in which bold, dark vertical bars are the distinctive elements of the melanin pattern, i.e., in which horizontal elements are absent, were ordered into the genus *Placidochromis*. However, this genus in which seven scientifically described species are included is very heterogeneous and it must not be assumed that we are faced with closely related species. One species, previously described as *Placidochromis milomo*, probably belongs in the genus *Eclectochromis* (see above) and for that reason was mentioned in that section (see *Eclectochromis milomo*). A clearly marked bar pattern is only exhibited by *P. johnstoni* and *P.* "Johnstoni Solo".

Other scientifically described species of this genus are *P. electra*, *P. hennydaviesae*, *P. longimanus*, *P. stonemani*, and *P. subocularis*.

In Tanzania, we found *P. johnstoni* and *P.* "Johnstoni Solo". These species are also known from Malawi. New species, only detected in Tanzania so far, are *P.* "Electra Makonde" and *P.* "Electra Blue Hongi", which because of their similarity to *P. electra* should be ordered into this genus. As for a fifth species that we found, we might be dealing with *P. phenochilus* (see *P. cf. phenochilus*).

# *Placidochromis* "Electra Blue Hongi"

### Name

This cichlid is commercially known as "Blue Hongi" (LEPEL 1993a). The addition "Electra" refers to the close relationship to *P. electra*. Another denotation is "New Deepwater Hap" (DEMASON 1994b; formerly *P. electra* was imported as "Deepwater Hap").

### Characteristics

Medium-sized, moderately high-backed cichlid, whose total length is usually ca 15 cm. Melanin patterning is either absent or sometimes consists of faint vertical barring. Females are a monochrome grey to brownish. Males show an overall metallic coloration. In particular, older males may take on a very strong blue, and occasionally exhibit a reddish anal fin.

### Distribution

We found this species at Lundo Island and Mbamba Bay (northern rocky coast, Luhuchi Rocks and Ngkuyo Island). LEPEL (1993a) mentioned Hongi Island as place of discovery.

### Habitat and feeding

We observed *P.* "Electra Blue Hongi" over sandy and pebbled substrates, rarely at the edge of mixed zones. Preferred depths appear to lie between 10 and 25 m. *P.* "Electra Blue Hongi" lived mostly in groups of about three to eight specimens, containing males as well as females.

116

These groups were not territorial, but covered vast distances. We were unable to observe territorial males. This species probably feeds chiefly on small invertebrates that live in the substrate. We frequently observed that *P.* "Electra Blue Hongi" picked up sand in its mouth and sifted it. Bottom-oriented species.

## Similar species

As already mentioned under Name, a certain similarity exists to *P. electra*. This species lives at Likoma and on Malawi's eastern coast (Makanjila/Fort Maguire). Based on our present knowledge, *P.* "Electra Blue Hongi", despite similar coloration and life style, is not a geographical form of *P. electra,* but an independent, albeit related species. *P.* "Electra Makonde", on the other hand, might be a geographical form of *P.* "Electra Blue Hongi" (see below).

*Placidochromis* "Electra Blue Hongi", female (Mbamba Bay)

*Placidochromis* "Electra Blue Hongi" (Mbamba Bay)

# *Placidochromis* "Electra Makonde"

## Name

This tentative name was chosen because of the resemblance to *Placidochromis electra* (see especially the underwater photograph from Makonde). At Makonde we were able to observe this species relatively often.

## Characteristics

Medium-sized cichlid with small mouth and laterally compressed, moderately elongated body. Total length ca 10 to 13 cm. Melanin pattern consists of trace of bars the first one of which — directly behind the gill cover — is usually the most conspicuous. Males bluish to dark-blue with yellowish belly and lower flank area. Females silvery-grey with blackish pelvic and anal fins. The lower edge of the caudal fin sometimes also carries black pigmentation.

## Distribution

This species is frequently found between Makonde and Lupingu. Probably also distributed north of Makonde up to the northern end of the lake.

## Habitat and feeding

As a rule, *P.* "Electra Makonde" lives on a sandy substrate. We frequently found this species over sandy or mixed substrates near rocks. The preferred depth appears to be between 15 and 25 m. Females swim in small troops which occasionally also contain males. Larger males, however, are usually solitary. The males possibly defend territories over sand during spawning. We observed that food is picked up from the bottom and also that sand is sifted for food. Hence, *P.* "Electra Makonde" lives primarily on invertebrates which live on or in the sand. Not a predatory species.

## Similar species

As mentioned above, this species shows similarities to *P. electra*. This becomes especially obvious if one includes females or subadults in the comparison. Nevertheless, we are dealing in this case with a separate species and not with a geographical form or subspecies of *P. electra*. As long as the relationship is not completely clarified, one should consider *P.* "Electra Makonde" as an independent species, to avoid misunderstandings.

Another cichlid, which on the basis of a similar life style and particularly due to its similar coloration and body shape, that is probably closely related to *P.* "Electra Makonde", is *P.* "Electra Blue Hongi" (see above). The latter species has been found at Hongi Island, Lundo Island, and Mbamba Bay. It is possible that *P.* "Electra Makonde" and *P.* "Blue Hongi" might be classified as location variants (= geographical races) of one species. Based on present knowledge, the estuary of the Ruhuri River might be the border between the two populations.

*Placidochromis* "Electra Makonde", male and female (Makonde)

*Placidochromis* "Electra Makonde", female (Lupingu)

*Placidochromis* "Electra Makonde", (Lupingu)

119

## Characteristics

Medium-sized, moderately high-backed cichlid with clearly marked bar pattern. Rarely exhibited: two longitudinal bands (fright coloration). Total length is ca 15 to 20 cm, rarely larger. Basic coloration of females is yellowish-grey to yellow. Dominant males show a blue-green head and bluish to yellow flanks. In the dorsal and caudal fins numerous yellowish to red pigment stripes are formed. The red portion appears to vary depending on food.

## Distribution

*P. johnstoni* is distributed in the entire lake and is also encountered in Lake Malombe as well as in the upper river Shire (ECCLES & TREWAVAS 1989: 115–117). We found this species in several sections of the Tanzanian coast (for example, frequently at Lupingu).

## Habitat and feeding

The preferred biotope of *P. johnstoni* consists of *Vallisneria* beds in shallow water of ca 3 m, less frequently over mixed sand/stone or purely stony substrates. Rarely encountered deeper than 15 m. Males or females are either solitary or live in mixed groups. We saw several males in breeding coloration, none of whom were territorial. One can observe *P. johnstoni* regularly foraging among *Vallisneria* beds. According to ECCLES & TREWAVAS (1989: 117) this species feeds on insects (larvae) and small fish.

## Similar species

A very similar species, with respect to body shape and pattern, is *P.* "Johnstoni Solo" (see below).

## Comments

*P. johnstoni* has been known in aquaristic circles for a long time.

*Placidochromis johnstoni,* female in a Vallisneria bed at Lupingu.

*Placidochromis johnstoni* in the rocky zone at Lupingu

*Placidochromis johnstoni* (aquarium photo)

*Placidochromis johnstoni* (Lupingu)

*Placidochromis johnstoni,* female (aquarium photo)

*Placidochromis johnstoni* (aquarium photo)

121

# *Placidochromis* "Johnstoni Solo"

## Name

The name goes back to KONINGS (1989: 178), who found this species at Chisumulu and on the west coast.

## Characteristics

Small to medium-sized, moderately high-backed cichlid which seldom attains a total length of more than 10 to 12 cm. Melanin pattern consists of usually six broad bars. Frequently there are also two longitudinal bands that run through the center and the upper half of the flank. Caudal and anal fin with blackish pigmentation, particularly in the male. Cheeks, throat and anterior chest area also have blackish pigmentation. Large males show blue sheen in upper head area and on the flanks.

## Distribution

Possibly widely distributed. On the Tanzanian coast, we found this species relatively often at Ikombe, Lumbira, and Kirondo. Also documented on the west coast and at Chisumulu (KONINGS 1989: 178). The author encountered this cichlid furthermore quite frequently at Nkhata Bay. Generally speaking, a rare species that one finds only irregularly while diving.

## Habitat and feeding

Rocky and mixed substrates ranging from shallow water to ca 15 to 20 m appear to be the preferred biotope of *P.* "Johnstoni Solo". At Ikombe, a mixed substrate prevailed with medium-sized to large boulders, while at Kirondo we observed this species in a rock-covered zone at about 10 m. We always saw *P.* "Johnstoni Solo" solitary. None of the individuals was territorial. Foraging for food, both males and females were seen roaming through the rocky littoral.

Due to its foraging behavior, *P.* "Johnstoni Solo" is easily recognized in the wild: the fish stops swimming, bends over forwards and examines the substrate very closely in order to find prey. It is probable that this species feeds on insect larvae and other small invertebrates which live in the Aufwuchs or sediment.

## Similar species

With respect to its melanin pattern, *P.* "Johnstoni Solo" is very similar to *P. johnstoni*. The latter can be differentiated by its longer snout. In the wild *P.* "Johnstoni Solo" can immediately be recognized due to its typical foraging behavior.

*Placidochromis* "Johnstoni Solo", juvenile (Lumbira)

*Placidochromis* "Johnstoni Solo" (Kirondo)

*Placidochromis* "Johnstoni Solo", foraging behavior (Nkhata Bay)

*Placidochromis* "Johnstoni Solo" (Ikombe)

123

# *Placidochromis* cf. *phenochilus*

### Name

These cichlids is probably conspecific with *"Haplochromis" phenochilus.*

### Characteristics

Medium-sized, high-backed cichlid. Total length ca 15 cm, rarely larger. Forehead line, particularly in larger animals, is slightly concave. The melanin pattern consists mostly of faint dark barring. Usually the first two bars are marked the strongest. Cheek area dark to dark-blue, but lips are light. Females are a uniform grey to brownish, males bluish to deep-blue, sometimes almost violet.

### Distribution

We detected this species at Makonde and Lupingu. Probably widely distributed around the Livingstone Mountains.

### Habitat and feeding

Mixed and sandy substrates at depths below 10 m. Only a few, solitary specimens could be observed by us. None of these animals was territorial. Foraging for food, they roamed over the lake bottom. Food is obtained from the uppermost sand or sediment layers.

### Similar species

It is obvious that this species exhibits a close relationship to *P. electra*, as evidenced by the blue coloration of the males, the melanin pattern and the entire body shape. *P. electra*, as its distinguishing trait, exhibits a straight or even convex forehead line.

### Comments

*"Haplochromis" phenochilus* was the only species which in the revision of Non-Mbunas (Eccles & Trewavas 1989: 318–319) could not be ordered within a new genus, the reason being that only one type specimen exists of this species, which is a male in breeding coloration, without recognizable melanin pattern. When males that are colored blue throughout are preserved, the color generally turns dark or black, so that the existing melanin patterns are obscured. Different melanin patterns, however, were precisely the basis for the establishment and definition of the new genera in the revision mentioned above; consequently, Eccles & Trewavas kept this species as *"Haplochromis" phenochilus.*

The only type of this species has white lips and a white mark on the snout. This specimen was caught on the northwest coast at Vua (Chilumba). The specimens observed by us exhibited lips that were not completely white but light. Unfortunately, nothing is known about the variational range of this species so we cannot assume with any certainty that these individuals might be considered conspecific with *"H." phenochilus*. Because of its similarity to *P. electra*, the population observed by us was ordered here in the genus *Placidochromis*.

*Placidochromis* cf. *phenochilus* (Makonde)

*Placidochromis* cf. *phenochilus* (Lupingu)

125

# The genus *Protomelas*

Eccles & Trewavas 1989

At present the genus *Protomelas* encompasses 14 scientifically described species. The representatives of this genus show a less well developed melanin pattern (called plesiomorph = original), consisting of two longitudinal bands and occasionally vertical elements. Of the two longitudinal bands, the first one is more pronounced and runs through the middle of the body. The second longitudinal band runs through the upper half of the body, roughly centered between the first one and the beginning of the dorsal. This melanin pattern is classified as original because it is also exhibited by several, comparatively primitive riverine cichlids and for this reason might have been the plesiomorphic melanin pattern.

*Protomelas* species usually attain a total length of 15 to 20 cm. Many species have lakewide distribution.

## *Protomelas annectens*

(Regan 1922)

### Characteristics

Medium-sized to large, relatively high-backed cichlid. Total length mostly around 15 cm, but also up to 20 cm and larger. The melanin pattern consists of a central black longitudinal band and fainter vertical bars. Dominant males are blue to black. Older males may exhibit elongated dorsal and anal fins. Females show a grey to brownish basic color. Some females sport an ochre-colored back.

### Distribution

*P. annectens* is known from the northwest (Chilumba) as well as from Malawi's east coast (Eccles & Trewavas 1989: 61). In Tanzania, we found this species at Magunga and Liuli. Probably wide distribution, but a rare species.

### Habitat and feeding

*P. annectens* predominantly inhabits sandy, rarely intermediate habitats. The preferred depth is not known, probably deeper than 10 m. The specimen shown, from Liuli, was caught by a fisherman's net in the sandy bay of Liuli. Underwater, we found this species only solitary. None of the specimens observed was territorial. *P. annectens* obtains food from the substrate which frequently is sifted for food. Sometimes one finds *P. annectens* in the company of *Taeniolethrinops praeorbitalis*. This cichlid digs through the substrate for prey and stirs up a lot of sand in the process. *P. annectens* then uses this opportunity to forage for small bottom-dwelling invertebrates.

**Similar species**

Other species, colored dark-blue in the male, are *Cyrtocara moori, Otopharynx selenurus, Placidochromis* (cf.) *phenochilus,* and the population of *Placidochromis electra* that lives on Malawi's east coast (Makanjila/Fort Maguire). All of these species prefer the sandy zone, but differ markedly in their melanin pattern.

*Protomelas annectens,* female (aquarium photo)

*Protomelas annectens* (aquarium photo)

*Protomelas annectens* (Liuli)

*Protomelas annectens* (Magunga)

127

# *Protomelas fenestratus*                                (TREWAVAS 1935)

## Characteristics

Medium-sized, relatively high-backed cichlid. Total length, as a rule, ca 12 to 14 cm, rarely larger. Melanin pattern decidedly variable: mostly vertical bars and two dark horizontal bands are formed, the latter being partially irregular. The vertical components usually dominate the pattern. Females with silvery-grey to yellowish basic coloration. Males blue with partially yellow body parts (geographical variation; see below).

## Distribution

This species is widely distributed in the entire lake (ECCLES & TREWAVAS 1989: 63). In Tanzania, we found *P. fenestratus* at nearly every coastal region (Ikombe, Nkanda, Kirondo, Makonde, Lupingu, Magunga, Cove Mountain, Ndumbi Reef, Pombo Reef, Lundu, Njambe, Tumbi Rocks, Tumbi Reef, Puulu Island, Hongi Island, Lundo Island, on the northern coast and Luhuchi Rocks at Mbamba Bay, Undu Point, and Hai Reef).

## Habitat and feeding

*P. fenestratus* inhabits stony and mixed substrates ranging from shallow water to a depth of about 25 m. Rarely can this species be found at greater depths. Males defend territories, which are about 1 m in diameter. The center of a territory is often a rock wall offering protection or larger rock crevices. The females mostly live in troops of three to ten specimens, which roam through the littoral and forage for food. *P. fenestratus* is a typical representative of the sediment-rich rocky zone.

Food is found chiefly in the substrate or in the sediment deposited on stones and rocks. A specialty of this species consists in directing — by mouth — a jet of water onto the bottom and whirling up the sediment to expose prey. To achieve this, the fish stands on its head at an angle of about 45 degrees or steeper and blows directly onto the substrate. By this "sandblasting" technique *P. fenestratus* is easily recognized in the wild. Interestingly enough it is the female who most frequently exhibits this behavior. We were not able to observe it in territory-defending males.

## Similar species

A very similar and also variable species is *Protomelas taeniolatus*. In recent aquaristic publications this species has frequently been confused with *P. fenestratus*. *P. taeniolatus* in the male sex is also blue, sometimes with yellow pigmentation, particularly in the chest and belly area. Some populations, in the male sex, show a pretty red coloration on the flanks (Senga Bay/Namalenji Island population; previously known commercially under the misleading name of "Haplochromis Boadzulu"). The melanin pattern in *P. taeniolatus* consists of two longitudinal bands, and in contrast to *P. fenestratus,* of fewer vertical bars which in addition rarely extend to the lower flanks. Furthermore, the barring elements are ordered more regularly than in *P. fenestratus*. In the wild, one can further distinguish *P. taeniolatus* from *P. fenestratus* in that this species does not engage in "sand-blasting" and rather prefers rocky, sediment-poor substrates (cf. ECCLES & TREWAVAS 1989: 64).

*P. fenestratus*, as well as *P. taeniolatus*, show a wide distribution in the lake. Highly diverse populations have been offered commer-

*Protomelas fenestratus* (Kirondo)

*Protomelas fenestratus* (Ikombe)

*Protomelas fenestratus* (Nkanda)

*Protomelas fenestratus,* female (Nkanda)

*Protomelas fenestratus* (Nkanda)

cially under the collective term of "Steveni". The Mbenji population of *P. taeniolatus* was originally denoted as "Steveni Mbenji". "Fire Blue" was the name given to *P. taeniolatus* of Likoma.

*P. fenestratus* from Malawi's east coast (Makanjila/Fort Maguire) was known under "Steveni Eastern". *P. fenestratus* populations with primarily broad-bar melanin patterns (for example, from Chisumulu Island) were imported as "Steveni Thick Bar", populations with irregular, narrow bars (for example, from Maleri Island), as "Steveni Tiger".

The populations listed in the following from Mara Rocks and Ngkuyo Island should probably be classified as local variants of *P. fenestratus* (see below).

## Comments

As already mentioned, in *P. fenestratus* we have a very variable species. The variability pertains primarily to the melanin pattern and the coloration of dominant males. Based on our investigations on the coast of Tanzania and in accordance with observations that the author was able to make on the coast of Malawi, the variability of the melanin pattern (with restrictions, see below) cannot be traced to geographical variants exclusively. This means that even within one defined population, at one location one can find females with extremely different melanin patterns (in the male the melanin pattern is mostly superimposed by the blue coloration). These differences can be so great that one could, when observing single individuals, easily get the wrong impression that this is a different species. Only when comparing the entire "spectrum" of melanin patterns within one population, is one able to see the variability. In rare cases, one can find females in groups, in which all "extremes" of melanin pattern variation are present.

The coloration of dominant males in one location is likewise subject to a certain range of fluctuation. In addition, in some cases there is also a population-specific, i.e., geographical variation of male coloration. The range of fluctuation within one population affects primarily the formation of yellow pigmentation on the flanks. The populations in the region of the Livingstone Mountains (Ikombe to Manda) are mostly uniformly blue with yellow lower body parts (throat, chest, and belly). Primarily in older males, the yellow pigmentation occurs in the areas of chest, neck, and anterior back. In principle, this coloration is also found in most other populations.

The clearest geographical variation is shown by the population of Pombo Reef. Here, the males exhibit an intensive yellow cheek area. Furthermore, the yellow coloration in the chest and belly area is relatively broad.

An example of a slight deviation from the usual male coloration appears to be the population of Puulu Island. Here, we predominantly found males who were conspicuous with regard to the yellow to golden edges of scales in rather large areas over their flanks; viewed from a distance, this made them appear completely yellow-golden. Apart from the Pombo Reef population the variation within different populations seemed greater to us than between the populations. Furthermore intensive investigations might yield the result that additional geographical variants exist.

*Protomelas fenestratus* (Pombo Reef)

*Protomelas fenestratus* (Tumbi Rocks)

*Protomelas fenestratus* (Puulu Island)

*Protomelas fenestratus,* female (Nkanda)

*Protomelas fenestratus,* "sandblasting" female
(Undu Point)

131

# Protomelas "Fenestratus Taiwan"

## Name

The name indicates the relationship of this population to *P. fenestratus*. "Taiwan Fenestratus" or "Taiwan Red" is the trade name for an evidently conspecific species from Taiwan Reef at Chisumulu Island (see below). A fantasy name for this cichlid in the trade is also *P.* "Chimoto Red" (LEPEL 1993b).

## Characteristics

Medium-sized, relatively high-backed cichlid. Total length ca 12 to 14 cm. With regard to body shape mostly identical with *P. fenestratus* (see above). Melanin pattern consists of mainly broad barring with hardly any horizontal elements. In young individuals, the second and third, as well as the fourth and fifth bars in the middle of the body are sometimes connected via a horizontal spot. Basic body color of females is silvery to grey. Dominant males show a blue head and back. Forehead usually with white blaze. Dorsal fin white or with broad white edge. Chest, lower flank area and pelvic fins yellow. The anal fin sports a broad red longitudinal stripe or edge.

## Distribution

The only population of these cichlids in Tanzania lives at Mara Rocks (Mbamba Bay). An appearently identical population was found on Taiwan Reef (Chisumulu Island) (KONINGS 1992: 136; SPREINAT 1993a). Another, very similar population lives at Ngkuyo Island (Mbamba Bay; see below).

## Habitat and feeding

The Mara Rocks (also called Ngkuyo Reef) form a deep area north of Ngkuyo Island at Mbamba Bay. A small part of the rock emerges from the water. The littoral consists primarily of large rocks, extending to a depth of at least 50 m. Down to about 20 m the rocks are not covered with a thick layer of sediment. Most males of "Fenestratus Taiwan" inhabit depths of about 10 to 20 m. They defend territories on rocky surfaces, which may be several meters in diameter. In some locations one may find one male next to another. The distances between males are about 3 to 4 m. Females were found solitary or in small troops. The "sandblasting" described for *P. fenestratus* (see above) was not observed. This can probably be traced to the nature of the substrate and should not be attributed to the specimens living here. Instead, we repeatedly observed that food was picked up from the rocky surface and that there was "plucking" at the Aufwuchs. Plankton was also consumed.

## Similar species

As already mentioned, a very similar population lives at Ngkuyo Island (see below: "Fenestratus Ngkuyo").

## Comments

It is noteworthy that a most probably identical population also lives on Taiwan Reef off Chisumulu Island. Mara Rocks and Taiwan Reef are both deep-water regions consisting of rocks that jut out from large depths and are isolated by deep water (more than 50 m) from other coastal sections.

The lifestyle of these populations with respect to settling on sediment-poor, large rocks and the "plucking" at algal mats corresponds to that of *P. taeniolatus*. Yet, everything points to the fact that this population we are dealing with, is a location variant or subspecies of *P. fenestratus*. *P. fenestratus* inhabits nearly the entire coast of Tanzania and consequently was encountered by us on the northern coast of Mbamba Bay as well as at Luhuchi Rocks (southern border of Mbamba Bay). It is only at Mara Rocks and at Ngkuyo Island where the "classical" *P. fenestratus* does not live, but instead we have "Fenestratus Taiwan" or "Fenestratus Ngkuyo". *P. taeniolatus*, by contrast, was not found at all in Tanzania. Regarding the melanin pattern, it must be added that *P. taeniolatus* shows more horizontal instead of vertical elements (cf. *P. fenestratus*; Similar species). The populations of Mara Rocks and Ngkuyo Island, however, correspond in their melanin pattern to the *P. fenestratus* population known under the trade name of "Steveni Thick Bar" (for example, from Chisumulu Island).

*Protomelas* "Fenestratus Taiwan" (Mara Rocks, Mbamba Bay)

*Protomelas* "Fenestratus Taiwan" (Mara Rocks, Mbamba Bay)

*Protomelas* "Fenestratus Taiwan", female (Mara Rocks, Mbamba Bay)

*Protomelas* "Fenestratus Taiwan", female (Mara Rocks, Mbamba Bay)

*Protomelas* "Fenestratus Taiwan", female (Taiwan Reef, Chisumulu Island)

*Protomelas* "Fenestratus Taiwan" (Taiwan Reef, Chisumulu Island)

# *Protomelas* "Fenestratus Ngkuyo"

At Ngkuyo Island, we found a population which, except for the coloration of the anal fin, appears to be identical with *P.* "Fenestratus Taiwan". The littoral of this island is comparable to that of Mara Rocks and *P.* "Fenestratus Ngkuyo" evidently occupies the same ecological niche as does the neighboring population at Mara Rocks. We could not discern any behavioral differences either.

The only difference that needs mentioning is that *P.* "Fenestratus Ngkuyo" does not have a red, but a yellow edge to its anal fin. We observed this difference in many specimens. To what degree the different coloration of the anal fin might be traceable to different food ingredients at the two locations must be the subject of future investigations.

*Protomelas* "Fenestratus Ngkuyo" at Ngkuyo Island (Mbamba Bay) and photographed in an aquarium (small photo)

# *Protomelas* cf. *pleurotaenia*

## Name

This cichlid is probably identical with *P. pleurotaenia*. Melanin pattern, body shape, size, and mouth structure as well as preferred lifestyle coincide to a large extent (cf. ECCLES & TREWAVAS 1989: 47).

## Characteristics

Medium-sized, relatively elongated cichlid with small mouth. High-backed in old age. Total length mostly 12 to 14 cm. The melanin pattern consists of a strongly marked central longitudinal band which, as a rule, is continuous. A second faint longitudinal band is sometimes present in the upper body half. The basic coloration of females is silvery to yellowish-green. Males are completely metallic blue. Anal fin blackish with broad yellow edge.

## Distribution

We found this cichlid at Lupingu, Manda, and Mbamba Bay. *P. pleurotaenia* probably has lake-wide distribution. Documented locations of this species are Monkey Bay, Nkhata Bay, Chilumba, Vua, and Karonga (ECCLES & TREWAVAS 1989: 47, 49).

## Habitat and feeding

*P.* cf. *pleurotaenia* prefers intermediate habitats at a depth of ca 3 to 10 m, interspersed with plants. We observed a small colony of this species at Lupingu, at a depth of only 3 m. The males had constructed sand nests. The rear of a sand nest was always located either adjacent to a small to medium-sized stone or in a field of plants. This species evidently begins the construction of a sand nest by transporting sand towards a stone or near the edge of a plant bed. The sand nests were not designed symmetrically. Starting at the stone or plant area, the surface of the hollow ran ramp-like to the top. The diameter of the hollow at the upper edge was about 30 to 40 cm, its height ca 20 to 30 cm. A perimeter of about 2 m around the nest was defended vehemently. Females that we observed over sand or mixed substrates were solitary. Food was picked up from the substrate. Some specimens foraged for edibles between Vallisnerias. Not a predatory species.

Beach life in the bay of Lupingu

*Protomelas* cf. *pleurotaenia* guarding his sand nest

*Protomelas* cf. *pleurotaenia*, female (Lupingu)

*Protomelas* cf. *pleurotaenia* (Lupingu)

137

# *Protomelas* "Spilonotus Tanzania"

## Name

This name is used commercially and refers to its similarity to *P. spilonotus*. However, *P.* "Spilonotus Tanzania" should not be considered conspecific with *P. spilonotus*.

## Characteristics

Medium-sized, moderately high-backed cichlid. Most specimens have a total length of ca 15 to 18 cm. The melanin pattern consists of a central longitudinal band that infrequently dissolves into three spots or blotches. The first blotch is usually formed by a connected "double" point. The second blotch is roughly above the middle area of the anal fin, and a third blotch is located on the caudal peduncle. A second longitudinal band, likewise dissolved into blotches, is sometimes recognizable in a faint form. Furthermore, black bars can sometimes be seen. The melanin pattern described applies especially to juveniles. In older specimens, the longitudinal band may also appear in the form of a loose row of dots. The ground color of females is silver-grey to brownish. Dominant males show an intensely blue head and body. Chest and belly are yellow-orange, as are the pelvic and anal fins.

## Distribution

We found this species at Ikombe and at Hongi Island. LEPEL (1994) reports that *P.* "Spilonotus Tanzania" frequently occurs at Lundo Island. It is probably distributed along the entire coast of Tanzania. No comparable population is known from Malawi as yet.

## Habitat and feeding

We found this cichlid in intermediate habitats with large boulders (Ikombe) and in the rocky zone (Hongi Island). The depth was around 2 to 15 m. Males in breeding colors were territorial and defended their territory in front of a backdrop of stones or rocks. At Hongi Island, *P.* "Spilonotus Tanzania" lived also in shallow water (2 to 3 m deep) but against the rock wall; when disturbed, it retreated into the rocks. We were not able to observe food consumption.

## Similar species

*P. spilonotus,* with respect to melanin pattern and body shape, is a very similar species. The melanin pattern of *P. spilonotus* likewise consists principally of two longitudinal bands and fainter cross bars, but the longitudinal bands tend to be continuous. The essential difference from *P.* "Spilonotus Tanzania" is the yellow forehead blaze of *P. spilonotus*. *P. spilonotus* was found by us in Tanzania at Kirondo. With respect to the breeding coloration of males, this population did not differ from the populations known from Malawi. Based on our own observations, *P. spilonotus* in Malawi does not show any geographical variation (coastal section of Mbenji Island, Maleri Island, Mumbo Island). Hence it is highly improbable that *P.* "Spilonotus Tanzania" represents a geographical variant of *P. spilonotus* because this would cause a conundrum as it would mean that this species which does not form geographical variants in Malawi conversely exhibits a high degree of variability in the connected coastal areas of Tanzania.

*Protomelas* "Spilonotus Tanzania" (aquarium photo)

Protomelas "Spilonotus Tanzania", female
(aquarium photo)

*Protomelas* "Spilonotus Tanzania" (Hongi Island);
photo: Dr. U. Ruß

*Protomelas* "Spilonotus Tanzania" (Ikombe)

*Protomelas spilonotus* (Mbenji Island, aquarium
photo)

# *Protomelas spilopterus*

### Characteristics

Medium-sized cichlid with robust and slightly protruding lower jaw. Total length mostly ca 15 to 20 cm. Melanin pattern consists of a central longitudinal band and a second, often only hinted at, longitudinal band between the beginning of the dorsal and the first band. Basic color of the female is silvery, grey or brownish. Dominant males are a uniform yellow to green-blue.

### Distribution

According to ECCLES & TREWAVAS (1989: 70) this species has a lake-wide distribution. In Tanzania, we found *P. spilopterus* at Makonde, Magunga, Pombo Reef, Tumbi Reef, and Mbamba Bay.

### Habitat and feeding

Rocky and intermediate areas form the preferred biotope. We found this species to be solitary and in shallow as well as in deep water up to ca 30 m. Males in breeding colors were not territorial and roamed slowly through the rocky littoral. We were not able to observe food consumption. EC-CLES & TREWAVAS (1989: 70) speculated that because of the slightly upwards turning mouth structure this fish could be a paedophage (feeding on larvae and young fry). A similar mouth structure (and also pharyngeal teeth) are exhibited also by *Caprichromis* spp., of which it has been reported that they zoom in from below on female mouthbrooders and then attack, with the goal of making them release their brood (MC-KAYE & KOCHER 1983).

### Similar species

From Malawi a species has become known which in body shape and melanin pattern close-ly resembles *P. spilopterus* ( *P.* "Spilopterus Blue"; KONINGS 1992: 235) and which is also widely distributed. The author found this species at Chitendi Island (Chilumba), Thumbi West Island (Cape Maclear), and at Likoma Island. This cichlid also lives on the Tanzanian coast and was observed by us at quite a few locations (for example, Tumbi Reef) together with *P. spilopterus*. The visible differences between the two "forms" are mostly restricted to the fact that *P.* "Spilopterus Blue" does not sport a very robust lower jaw and that the central longitudinal band usually does not extend all the way to the operculum, but breaks off a few centimeters before that. At the present level of knowledge we must assume that we are dealing with two independent species.

Fisherman at Ngkuyo Island

*Protomelas spilopterus* (Pombo Reef)

*Protomelas spilopterus* (Pombo Reef)

*Protomelas spilopterus* (Makanjila/Fort Maguire)

*Protomelas* "Spilopterus Blue" (Makonde)

*Protomelas* "Spilopterus Blue", female with fry (Tumbi Reef)

# The genus *Stigmatochromis*  ECCLES & TREWAVAS 1989

In this genus moderately elongate, predatory cichlids are ordered whose common features are a three-spot melanin pattern (cf. the genus *Otopharynx*) and a slightly projecting lower jaw. Scientifically described species are *S. woodi, S. modestus, S. pholidophorus,* and *S. pleurospilus.* While the first three species are known in aquaristic circles, the identity of *S. pleurospilus* is not clear. This cichlid has been described in only one specimen, which was a juvenile with a standard length (without caudal fin) of 4 cm and which stemmed from the northern end of the lake. It would be very difficult indeed to determine which cichlids in the lake correspond to this particular juvenile.

In Tanzania, we found the first three species described as well as another species which is traded under the name of *S.* "Cave". The latter was found at Nkanda, Lumbira, and Liuli.

## *Stigmatochromis modestus*  (GÜNTHER 1893)

### Characteristics

Medium-sized, moderately elongate cichlid. Total length ca 15 cm, rarely up to 20 cm. Melanin pattern consists of three relatively small spots which due to the dark pigmentation are rarely visible. Basic coloration light to dark-brown. Males mostly with blue sheen. Males in breeding colors may be dark-blue with red anal fin.

### Distribution

Widely distributed species, but occurring nowhere in large numbers (ECCLES & TREWAVAS 1989: 175). In Tanzania, found relatively frequently in the area of the Livingstone Mountains.

### Habitat and feeding

*S. modestus* is found over stony and rocky substrates, rarely over mixed substrates. This cichlid inhabits a large range in the water column, i.e., from shallow water (3 m) to at least 35 m. *S. modestus* lives relatively hidden and because of its inconspicuous brown coloration is relatively hard to find. Dominant males that defend their territory in front of a stone crevice or small cave are rather conspicuous in comparison. *S. modestus* probably feeds primarily on other fish, i.e., it is a predator.

### Similar species

From Malawi's east coast (region of Makanjila/Fort Maguire), a cichlid under the trade name of *S.* "Modestus Eastern" (KONINGS 1992: 192) has become known which is very similar in body shape and melanin pattern. In contrast to *S. modestus* this species exhibits a rather silvery-grey basic coloration. The *S. modestus* seen by us at the Tanzanian coast completely (i.e., with respect to coloration) corresponded to those specimens known from different populations in Malawi.

*Stigmatochromis modestus* (aquarium photo)

*Stigmatochromis modestus* (aquarium photo)

*Stigmatochromis modestus* (Nakanthenga)

*Stigmatochromis* "Modestus Eastern" (aquarium photo)

*Stigmatochromis* "Cave" (Lumbira)

143

# *Stigmatochromis pholidophorus*  (Trewavas 1935)

### Characteristics

Medium-sized, elongated cichlid which usually attains a total length of ca 14 to 15 cm. Characteristic feature is the rounded (convex) and relatively steeply sloping forehead, with a kink above the eye, giving the impression of a "hooked nose". The melanin pattern consists of the genus-typical three spots. Usually there is also a row of dark spots at the base of the dorsal. Basic body color is silvery-grey. Dominant males show a uniform iridescent blue to green coloration. Sexually active males also exhibit blackish lower body parts.

### Distribution

Probably widely distributed. On the coast of Tanzania, we found this species at Lupingu. Furthermore, *S. pholidophorus* can also be found in Senga Bay and relatively often on the east coast of Malawi in the region of Makanjila/Fort Maguire (Spreinat 1993c). The type specimen on which this species description is based hails from Vua on the northwest coast (Eccles & Trewavas 1989: 178).

### Habitat and feeding

Intermediate habitats ranging from shallow water to depths of ca 10 m appear to be the preferred biotope of *S. pholidophorus*. Only rarely did we find this species at greater depths. None of the specimens observed was territorial. *S. pholidophorus* was always found solitary. We were not able to observe males in breeding coloration. In the author's aquarium a male — a few days before and during spawning — showed marked territorial behavior and defended its area in front of a stone cave against all other fish.

The behavior during foraging is noteworthy: at a distance of 20 to 30 cm this species inspects — usually in a bent-over forward position — stone crevices or other hiding places on the lake bottom. Before striking, the body is curved into a slight S-shape (Spreinat 1993c). From aquarium observations, it is known that *S. pholidophorus* is a predatory species which prefers to prey on juveniles.

### Similar species

Young specimens of *Exochochromis anagenys*, due to their elongated body shape and identical melanin pattern, exhibit similarities to *S. pholidophorus*, except that in *E. anagenys* the upper jaw is somewhat longer than the lower jaw, while *S. pholidophorus* has a shorter upper jaw.

### Comments

In a recent publication the author denoted this species as *S.* cf. *pholidophorus* (Spreinat 1993c). After having had the opportunity in Tanzania to investigate specimens from the north of the lake (the type of this species stems from the northwest of the lake), membership in the species has presumably been sufficiently proved.

*Stigmatochromis pholidophorus* (aquarium photo)

*Stigmatochromis pholidophorus,* female (Lupingu)

*Stigmatochromis pholidophorus*
(aquarium photo)

*tigmatochromis pholidophorus,* subadult
(aquarium photo)

*Stigmatochromis pholidophorus,* female
(Makanjila/Fort Maguire)

# *Stigmatochromis woodi*  (REGAN 1922)

## Characteristics

Large, moderately elongated cichlid with pointed head. Total length usually 20 cm, but specimens of 30 cm have been known. Melanin pattern has genus-typical three spots. Furthermore, a row of dark spots is visible at the base of the dorsal. Basic coloration of body whitish to silvery-grey. Dominant males show a mostly greenish-golden basic coloration with blackish lower body parts.

## Distribution

*S. woodi* is distributed lake-wide, but apparently nowhere in large numbers (ECCLES & TREWAVAS 1989: 178). In Tanzania we found this species at Tumbi Reef and Lundo Island.

## Habitat and feeding

*S. woodi* prefers mixed or primarily sandy regions. With respect to the preferred depth range, this species appears to be very adaptable. Depending on the conditions of the substrate we found *S. woodi* primarily between 5 and 30 m. According to ECCLES & TREWAVAS (1989: 178), *S. woodi* has been caught even at depths of 70 m. All specimens that we encountered were solitary and not territorial. Males in full breeding coloration were not among them. It is known that *S. woodi* is a predatory cichlid.

## Similar species

At the end of the 1980s a very similar species was found at Mbenji Islands and was called *S.* "Tolae" ("Spitzkopf Woodi"; cf. KONINGS 1992: 257; SPREINAT 1993c). This cichlid's head is even more pointed than that of *S. woodi*. Dominant *S.* "Tolae" begin to show black coloration,

starting at the underside. Males in full breeding colors may be uniformly black. Younger specimens of both species are hard to distinguish since *S. woodi* in particular is variable with respect to the head profile.

Lundo Island

*Stigmatochromis woodi*, female (Tumbi Reef)

*Stigmatochromis woodi* (aquarium photo)

*Stigmatochromis woodi* (aquarium photo)

*Stigmatochromis woodi,* subadult
(aquarium photo)

*Stigmatochromis* "Tolae" (aquarium photo)

*Stigmatochromis* "Tolae" (aquarium photo)

147

# The genus *Tyrannochromis*

As the genus name aptly suggests, representatives of the genus *Tyrannochromis* are large-size predatory cichlids. In their revision of the earlier "Haplochromis" ECCLES & TREWAVAS (1989: 9–103) listed four species in this genus: *T. macrostoma, T. nigriventer, T. maculiceps,* and *T. polyodon.* However, the species status of the latter two is by no means certain: to all appearances they are younger synonyma for *T. macrostoma.*

In Tanzania we found *T. macrostoma* as well as *T. nigriventer.*

## *Tyrannochromis macrostoma* (REGAN 1922)

### Characteristics

Large, elongate cichlid with large mouth, which can attain a total length of ca 30 cm. Melanin pattern consists of two longitudinal bands, of which the first, central one is always formed, yet is not all that visible since the lower flank is also dark-brown to blackish. The second longitudinal band, which is centered in the upper flank half, often only exists in the form of a row of faint dots. At the base of the dorsal there is a row of dark spots. The basic color of juveniles is silvery-grey. At a size of about 8 to 9 cm the lower half of the flank and the head below the eye begin to turn dark-brown, nearly black. The upper half of the flank remains light. Under stress conditions, the dark pigmentation of the lower body half fades. Males in full breeding coloration show a bluish back and/or upper flank area. The lower flank half is blackish with a blue sheen. Throat, chest, and belly exhibit yellow pigment.

### Distribution

*T. macrostoma* probably have lake-wide distribution. No data have been published on Mozambique's coastline, but on the basis of relative frequency on all the other coasts one can safely assume that this cichlid also inhabit the coasts of Mozambique. The author found this species during nearly every dive made on the coast of Malawi. The same was true for the coast of Tanzania.

### Habitat and feeding

Rocky and intermediate habitats, less often regions with plants, are among the biotopes in which one encounters *T. macrostoma.* Only broad sandy regions seem to be avoided. The distribution of *T. macrostoma* varies between shallow water and depths of at least 40 m. This species is solitary, roaming over the substrate without territorial bonds and is constantly searching for potential prey. Since we did not see males in full breeding coloration, statements on possible territorial behavior of the male cannot be made.

*T. macrostoma* is a predatory fish which approaches its prey in a typical manner. As soon as a potential victim has been sighted, the predator turns about 90 degrees to the side, so as to

*Tyrannochromis macrostoma*

*Tyrannochromis macrostoma*, female

*Tyrannochromis macrostoma*, female (Pombo Reef)

*Tyrannochromis macrostoma*, juvenile (aquarium photo)

*Tyrannochromis macrostoma*, school of juveniles (Chitendi Island, Chilumba)

149

catch his prey by striking rapidly from above at an oblique angle. This behavior we observed quite frequently; many attempts of the predator were unsuccessful, however, and rarely did we see *T. macrostoma* swim away with wriggling prey in its mouth.

*T. macrostoma* females care for their fry for a relatively long time. Frequently, we were able to observe how a female released its fry of about 2 to 3 cm, on or at the edge of a rock and then started to defend this region vigorously against all other fish. Meanwhile the fry were feeding. At perceived threats from the observer the fry were immediately returned to the mouth of the female and the female swam to another spot. It is noteworthy that the swarm of fry often contained heterospecific juveniles, which were also cared for by the female. It is not known when the female's instinct for caring for her brood ends. We had the impression that the female does not always return all fry to her mouth so that at least part of the fry was set free.

**Similar species**

Other species which were described a long time ago and placed in this genus by ECCLES & TRE-WAVAS (1989: 97–103), are *T. maculiceps* (AHL 1927: type locality: Langenburg = Lumbira) and *T. polyodon* (TREWAVAS 1935: type locality: Vua). For *T. nigriventer* see the text below. The two first-named species were described in each case on the basis of only one single specimen. They differed from *T. macrostoma* due to morphological or morphometrical properties (*T. maculiceps*: narrower head and more rows of teeth; *T. polyodon*: greater body depth). At the present time there are many indications that these differences from *T. macrostoma* (this species too was described on the basis of only one individual) — once a representative number of specimens has been examined — will fall within the variational range of *T. macrostoma*.

Then these two species will be considered junior synonyms since they were described later than *T. macrostoma*.

**Comments**

Until recently the identity of *T. macrostoma* was unclear and more than confusing. At the end of the 1980s and the beginning of the 1990s, the author was in close contact with E. TREWAVAS in order to clarify which cichlid in the lake corresponds to the species described as *Haplochromis macrostoma* by REGAN in 1922.

Since roughly the beginning of the 1980s, a predatory cichlid was known in aquaristic trade under the name of *Haplochromis macrostoma*. After the author had an opportunity to examine the type of this species in the British Museum (Natural History), it became evident that the cichlid denoted by "H. macrostoma" in the trade could not possibly be identical with this species. Consequently, the question arose which cichlid is *Haplochromis macrostoma* (today *Tyrannochromis macrostoma*)? At this time, it was known that two similar, predatory species occur at many coastal sections: one species was characterized by a dark lower body half, and was named by the author with the provisional name "Schwarzbauch" (English "Dark Belly"). The second species was the cichlid with the trade name "H. macrostoma". The lower half of the body in this "Trade Macrostoma" is pale and so this species can usually be immediately differentiated from the "Schwarzbauch" because of this characteristic.

In order to clarify the species affiliation and to classify the result of the field investigation, the author presented a number of specimens to the British Museum for differentiation. One of the problems that arose was that the "Schwarzbauch" lost its dark pigmentation when subjected to stress, thereby becoming similar to the "Trade-Macrostoma". Also none

*Tyrannochromis macrostoma*, female (aquarium photo)

*Tyrannochromis macrostoma*, juvenile (Chitendi Island, Chilumba)

*Tyrannochromis macrostoma*, female (Likoma Island)

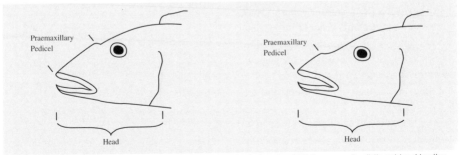

*Tyrannochromis macrostoma* (left) and *Tyrannochromis nigriventer* (right) are easily distinguished by the relative lengthes of their premaxillary pedicels.

of the preserved types in the British Museum showed a dark lower half of the body, so that this criterion could not be used to determine whether a "Schwarzbauch" was present under the described species or not. TREWAVAS found a small morphological characteristic which differentiated the two species, namely the length of the dorsal prolongation of the premaxillary pedicel. Even in the living fish, the upper end of this bone can be seen/felt as a small bump on the "nose" situated roughly below the level of the eyes. This bone is very long in the "Schwarzbauch" and comparatively short in the "Trade Macrostoma" (see below). When a comparison was made to the type specimens, it was shown that the "Schwarzbauch" should be considered as being conspecific with *T. macrostoma*, while the "Trade Macrostoma" belongs to an undefined species.

Parallel to and before the end of the previously cited investigations, ECCLES worked on the completion of a revision of this genus. He came to the erroneous conclusion that the "Schwarzbauch" belonged to an undescribed species and gave it the name *T. nigriventer* (Latin: nigriventer = black belly; ECCLES 1989a). A single specimen from the British Museum was the only type example used by ECCLES. The original colors present in living fish were obviously not known, as this specimen due to the length of its premaxillary pedicel can now be shown not to be a "Schwarzbauch" but a "Trade Macrostoma". As a consequence of this, the initial description of this type, although ist does not concern a "Schwarzbauch" as the name of the species indicates, still describes a new, at that time, scientifically unknown cichlid (cf. TREWAVAS 1991).

The taxonomy of the two species can be summarized as follows: the "Schwarzbauch" is *T. macrostoma*, while the cichlid known for a long time as "Trade Macrostoma" is *T. ni-*

*griventer*. Both species can be easily differentiated when living: *T. macrostoma* is dark in the lower half of the body whilst *T. nigriventer* is pale in this region. Nontypically colored specimens (stress) as well as totally blue or blackish males can be differentiated by the comparative lengths of the upper projection of the premaxillary pedicel. If the distance from the tip of the upper jaw to the "nose hump" below the eye is measured in *T. macrostoma*, this length is greater than a third of the total head length (nose tip to end of operculum). In *T. nigriventer*, this length is obviously smaller and is less than a third of the total head length.

## Characteristics

Large, elongate cichlid. Total length usually ca 20 to 25 cm, rarely up to 30 cm. Regarding the melanin pattern, two geographical forms can be distinguished. The southern populations exhibit two longitudinal bands of which the first, central band is continuous and usually broader. The second longitudinal band lies between the first and the base of the dorsal fin and sometimes is only faintly visible or dissolved into a row of spots. Another row of partially irregular spots is usually formed at the base of the dorsal fin. This feature is also present in the northern populations. The northern populations show no longitudinal-band pattern, but mostly irregular vertical bars.

For the exact distribution of northern and southern populations see Comments.

The basic coloration is variable and mostly varies between silvery-grey, beige, and brownish. Occasionally very dark specimens occur that appear to be uniformly brown or nearly black. Dominant males exhibit many shades, ranging from light-blue to dark-blue, sometimes even violet coloration. The throat and chest area are frequently yellow to orange. Juveniles are whitish to grey and exhibit the above population-specific melanin pattern very clearly.

## Distribution

*T. nigriventer* probably has lake-wide distribution. The author found this species at nearly all

*Tyrannochromis nigriventer* (Lupingu)

coastal sections of Malawi (Boadzulu Island, Monkey Bay, Eccles Reef, Thumbi West Island, Maleri Islands, Makanjila/Fort Maguire, Mbenji Islands, Nkhata Bay, Usisya, Chilumba, Likoma, and Chisumulu Island). In Tanzania we also found this cichlid at many coastal sections (Makonde, Lupingu, Cove Mountain, Lundu, Njambe, Mbamba Bay).

### Habitat and feeding

*T. nigriventer* lives on rocky and mixed substrates in shallow water down to depths of at least 30 m. Although most specimens are encountered in shallow water down to 10 m. *T. nigriventer* is solitary and roams tirelessly through the rocky littoral foraging for prey. Males in full breeding colors, however, are usually territorial. Frequently, areas in front of large stones or rocks are defended as territories against other, large fish. Depending on the size of the male, these territories are about 3 to 4 m in diameter.

*T. nigriventer* is a predator which primarily feeds on small fish. In contrast to *T. macrostoma*, *T. nigriventer* does not turn sideways during stalking, but catches his prey by direct zooming in and sudden striking.

The behavior of the female regarding care of her brood corresponds to that of *T. macrostoma* (see above).

### Similar species

*T. macrostoma* is very similar with respect to body shape. As a rule, the two species can be distinguished due to the dark coloration on the lower flank in *T. macrostoma* and the light flank coloration of *T. nigriventer*. Some specimens that are completely dark as well as males that are wholly blue, can be distinguished by comparing the length of the premaxillary pedicel (cf. *T. macrostoma*, Comments).

### Comments

The previously described variability of the melanin pattern is noteworthy. The southern populations characterized by two longitudinal bands were seen by the author at the following coastal sections: Boadzulu Island, Monkey Bay, Thumbi West Island, Mumbo Island, Chinyankhwazi and Chinyamwezi Island, Eccles Reef, Makanjila/Fort Maguire, Nakanthenga Island, Namalenji Island, Mbenji Island, Likoma, and Chisumulu Island. The northern populations begin at Nkhata Bay on the west coast and stretch at least to Chewere (north of Chilumba) on the northwest coast. They also extend over the entire Tanzanian coast from its northern end to at least Mbamba Bay. All these populations show an irregular pattern of vertical bars.

It is interesting that the populations along Malawi's eastern coast exhibit the pattern of longitudinal bands. Perhaps we can assume that on the east coast belonging to Mozambique there is either a coastal section on which an "intermediate" form exists or, for example, a long sandy beach forms a line separating the northern and southern populations. So far no related investigations from Mozambique have become known but one must assume that such a demarcation line, if it exists, would lie at least at the latitude of Likoma, since the populations of Likoma have the pattern of longitudinal bands.

*Tyrannochromis nigriventer* (Chilumba, aquarium photo)

*Tyrannochromis nigriventer*, female (Lupingu)

*Tyrannochromis nigriventer*, female (Njambe)

*Tyrannochromis nigriventer*, subadult (Chewere, Chilumba)

*Tyrannochromis nigriventer*, female (Likoma Island)

*Tyrannochromis nigriventer* (southern form, aquarium photo)

*Tyrannochromis nigriventer* (southern form, aquarium photo)

*Tyrannochromis nigriventer*, mouthbrooding female (Chinyamwezi Island)

*Tyrannochromis nigriventer*, subadult (Mumbo Island)

*Tyrannochromis nigriventer*, female (Boadzulu Island)

156

# Mbunas

The mostly vibrantly colored, rock-dwelling cichlids of Lake Malawi are called "Mbuna" by native fishermen. This name, from the tribal language of the Tonga (= Kitonga), was adopted early by aquarists and scientists alike, and has been generally accepted. All Mbunas are endemic to Lake Malawi and to some extent also to the upper Shire, which drains Lake Malawi in the south. This means that these species occur only in Lake Malawi (and the Shire region).

Although the concept of "Mbuna" unambiguously describes a certain group of cichlids, it is very difficult to name easy-to-comprehend criteria which help one to recognize a Mbuna. The most frequently cited criterion for distinguishing Mbunas from other cichlids is the formation of "genuine egg spots" in the anal fin of Mbuna males (e.g., ECCLES & TREWAVAS 1989: 21).

As "genuine egg spots", one considers only those that are marked by either a dark or a light edge. This is important insofar as many other cichlids in Lake Malawi have egg spots (or egg spot-like markings or stripes) in the anal fin of the male. These cichlids were previously classified under the collective genus of "Haplochromis". Only recently (1989) a taxonomic revision of the "Haplochromis" appeared and since then the term "Non-Mbuna" has been in use for the definition of this group (ECCLES & TREWAVAS 1989). Unfortunately, occasionally even Non-Mbunas exhibit a dark edge around their egg spots; thus a differentiation based on egg spots done is not always reliable. (For the interested reader, another morphological identification feature that can be used is the scales although even this criterion is fraught with uncertainties: in Mbunas the reduction in scale size between the chest and the flank area is rather abrupt and not gradual.)

In order not to give the wrong impression, it should be emphasized that on the whole it is simple to distinguish a Mbuna from a Non-Mbuna. The experience of knowing what a Mbuna "looks like" is quite sufficient for this purpose. Apart from very few exceptions, there is no doubt whatsoever about the correct classification of the more than 250 currently known Mbuna spp.

At present, we distinguish 10 Mbuna genera:

| | |
|---|---|
| *Cyathochromis* | 1 species |
| *Cynotilapia* | ca 14 species |
| *Genyochromis* | 1 species |
| *Gephyrochromis* | 4 species |
| *Iodotropheus* | 2 species |
| *Labeotropheus* | 2 species |
| *Labidochromis* | ca 30 species |
| *Melanochromis* | ca 24 species |
| *Petrotilapia* | ca 21 species |
| *Pseudotropheus* | ca 170 species |

Another, eleventh, Mbuna genus was described in 1975 under the name of *Microchromis* (sole species: *M. zebroides*) (JOHNSON 1975).

However, this genus description is lacking in precision and therefore is generally not acknowledged. Furthermore, the species *M. zebroides*, described at that time as allegedly coming from Likoma Island, has never been found again.

The word "circa" in the above table pertains to the fact that in many cases it is not clear whether the two (or more) similar populations found at different locations should be classified as location variants of one species or should be considered independent species.

157

## Variable Mbunas

Mbunas are small to medium-sized cichlids. Most species reach total lengths of 10 to 12 cm. The great majority of Mbunas exhibit a strictly rock-associated life style. Rocky or stony substrates offer these species protection against predators as well as food. Nearly all Mbunas are specialized in feeding on Aufwuchs, which is the conglomeration of algae and bacteria, including the associated micro-organisms, that forms a mat over hard substrates. Aufwuchs is hence not merely vegetable food. Aufwuchs feeders, when grazing on rocks, absorb numerous micro-organisms, from tiny protozoa to small crustaceans, snails, molluscs, and diverse insect larvae. Nonetheless, the vegetable components of Aufwuchs serve as "ballast", since these substances are digested slowly or with great difficulty. This means that Mbunas are not pure carnivores and thus should be given a ballast-rich diet in the aquarium. In diets containing only meat (e.g., beef heart), Mbunas quickly contract illnesses of the digestive tract. Moderate feeding with the addition of plant components are thus very important.

The rock-associated life style requires a relatively high allegiance to a particular location. A large sandy zone bordering on a rocky or stony region, as a rule, will not be crossed but forms an obstacle or "geographical" barrier. The result is that neighboring populations that are isolated from each other evolve in different ways; this is shown, for example, by the formation of different colorations. These color differences may be abrupt or gradual. Populations that are easy to differentiate in terms of color, are usually called **location variants** or **geographical races**. If the differences are very large, one speaks of a subspecies. As for a classification into location variants, geographical races, subspecies, and finally species, no universal agreement exists. Depending on the scientist, different standards are employed. The crucial point is which species concept is used for the definition of the taxon "species", since all further classifications depend on this definition. The above considerations pertain to populations which do not overlap in their distribution (allopatric populations).

It should be pointed out that "artificial" reefs, which can be established in a sandy zone, are also colonized by Mbunas, i.e., sandy regions do not present an insurmountable obstacle. Little is known about the mechanisms of the distribution of Mbunas and on the colonization of new biotopes. It is quite conceivable that juveniles that are hiding in torn-off vegetation are taken by currents to other parts of the coast.

Another aspect is that not all species that must be classified as strictly rock-associated have formed location variants. Such an example is *Petrotilapia tridentiger*, which lives rock-associated and can be found on many sections of the coast. Despite this fact no location variants have developed, the males and females in both the south and the north have generally the same coloration. In contrast, *Pseudotropheus* "Msobo" from Tanzania exhibits numerous location variants in a relatively small coastal section (see below).

Another phenomenon in the group of Mbunas is called **polymorphism** (= diverse forms) or to be more precise, **polychromatism** (= many colors). This refers to the formation of different body colors. The prerequisites are that the specimens in question are members of one species, the same sex, and must also inhabit the same biotope. A well-known example is *Pseudotropheus zebra*. The males are predominantly light-blue with black vertical bars, the females are grey-brown and also have a barred melanin pattern. In addition, one frequently sees specimens that have no bar pattern but instead

158

numerous dark blotches on light to reddish background. Such individuals are called OB morphs (for "orange-blotched"; the term "chrome" would have been more exact than "morph", but this word is not common). Analogously, the first-described normal form is called BB morph (blue-black). OB morphs occur more frequently in the female, while male OB morphs are rare. For *P. zebra* a third morph is known, which is colored a uniform whitish to reddish shade, has no body blotches and consequently is called an O morph. O morphs do occur in both sexes, but male O morphs are even more rare than OB males. An important criterion for the definition of color morphs is that no fluid transitions exist between them, i.e., there are clearly recognizable separate colors. In this respect the O morph is not a "true" morph. Nearly all O specimens have small black pigment spots.

Another example of polychromatism is exhibited by *P. callainos*. In this species, both sexes have a B morph (blue; completely light-blue), a W morph (colored a uniform white), and an OB morph (white with dark blotches).

A special case of polychromatism is **sexual dichromatism**. *P.* "Daktari", for example, exhibits a marked sexual dichromatism: the males are lemon-yellow, while the females are grey to brown. Occasionally this species also has yellowish females so that the above general statement needs qualification. Here it must be mentioned that subdominant males frequently assume the female coloration. In general, though, most Mbunas show a clear sexual dichromatism, whereas the formation of color morphs is limited to a few species. Polychromatism is particularly frequent in representatives of the *P. zebra* species-complex, in the genera *Labeotropheus* and *Genyochromis* as well as in some species from the *P. tropheops* species-group. Accordingly, there are three important aspects concerning the "variability" of Mbuna species that must be taken into consideration in a comparison of species: location variants or geographical races, polychromatism, and sexual dichromatism.

# The genus *Cyathochromis*

The genus *Cyathochromis* contains only one species: *C. obliquidens*. Because its teeth differ clearly from those of all other Mbunas, this species was placed in its own genus. The teeth of *C. obliquidens* are remarkably long-stemmed and show a spoon-like top.

In aquaristic terms *C. obliquidens* is not very important, since this species is seldom imported and raised. It is known that *C. obliquidens* is assertive and therefore should be kept in a large tank (minimum 1.5 m side length) and only in the company of other robust Mbunas.

# *Cyathochromis obliquidens*

### Characteristics

Relatively large Mbuna which can reach a total length of 15 cm. The teeth (cf. general description) are characteristic. Also conspicuous is the broad black band in the dorsal fin. Males in breeding colors usually show (dependent on location) a yellow back and partially yellow chest area. The lower body half is blue. Females and juveniles are grey-yellowish and show a melanin pattern consisting of a central lateral band and a second one in the upper body half that is usually only suggested by a row of dots. Even the central lateral band is occasionally only formed as a row of spots. In fully colored males, the melanin pattern is often superimposed and barely recognizable.

### Distribution

From the research of RIBBINK and coworkers, it is known that this species is widely distributed along the coast of Malawi provided suitable biotopes exist (RIBBINK et al. 1983: 242–243). This also applies to the coastal areas of Tanzania: we found this cichlid along the northern coast at the foot of the Livingstone Mountains as well as in the south at Mbamba Bay. Thus it can be assumed that, in all probability, *C. obliquidens* has lake-wide distribution.

### Habitat and feeding

A typical inhabitant of shallow water who prefers the intermediate zone of ca 1 to 2 m and is also frequently found in Vallisneria beds. Seldom found at depths deeper than 5 m. Males are aggressively territorial. Females are found solitary or in small groups. *C. obliquidens* feeds on Aufwuchs and small invertebrates.

### Similar species

At first glance *C. obliquidens* reminds one of *Petrotilapia* spp., but differs from the latter in its teeth, which can even be recognized with the naked eye. All things considered, the chances of confusion are slim.

*Cyathochromis obliquidens* (Mbamba Bay)

*Cyathochromis obliquidens* (aquarium photo)

*Cyathochromis obliquidens,* female in shallow water (Lupingu)

*Cyathochromis obliquidens* (Pontoon, Mbamba Bay)

*Cyathochromis obliquidens* (Magunga)

161

Representatives of the genus *Cynotilapia* are, with respect to coloration and melanin pattern as well as to body shape, nearly identical to the species from the *Pseudotropheus zebra* species-complex. However, in contrast to *Pseudotropheus* spp., all *Cynotilapia* have relatively widely-spaced, unicuspid teeth (*Pseudotropheus* spp. have relatively tightly spaced, bicuspid teeth). In larger specimens the unicuspid teeth can be easily recognized, even without a magnifying glass.

*Cynotilapia* spp. feed primarily on plankton. For gripping and holding on to this prey, one-cusp "dog teeth" are of course more suitable than comparatively blunt bicuspid teeth. The latter serve the *Pseudotropheus* spp. literally for "grazing" on Aufwuchs. In the wild, this way of feeding — fairly unusual in comparison to other Mbunas — is clearly reflected in behavior. *Cynotilapia*, as a rule, swim about 1 m above the rocky substrate, i.e., do not hover closely above rock or stones like most of the *Pseudotropheus* spp. Where the current is strong, one can sometimes find gigantic schools of *Cynotilapia afra* hovering in open water and feeding on plankton carried aloft by the current. Exceptions are sexually mature males, who stay close to the bottom in order to defend their territory. While they occasionally leave their territory to feed on plankton, one can frequently observe them plucking at Aufwuchs. Consequently, in the stomachs of territorial males Aufwuchs ingredients and insect larvae were found more frequently than in those of nonterritorial specimens (RIBBINK et al. 1983: 236–237).

Fourteen species are known from Malawi, only two of which have been described scientifically. The best known and presumably most widely distributed species is *C. afra*. The second described species is *C. axelrodi*. This species has been imported in Germany under the incorrect name *Pseudotropheus* "Kingsizei" (ZIERZ 1973, GERHARDT & SPREINAT 1989; the term *P.* "Kingsizei" is now being used for another cichlid). The other species of this genus are of lesser importance for aquarists. In Tanzania we found two species: *C. afra* and *C.* "Lion". All the presently known species with their distribution areas are compiled in the following table (the references cited refer to the data for coastal sections in Malawi).

Members of the genus *Cynotilapia* are characterized by their relatively wide-spaced unicuspid teeth (*Cynotilapia afra* at Lundo Island).

## *Cynotilapia* species and their distribution in Lake Malawi

| Species | Reference | Distribution |
|---------|-----------|--------------|
| *C. afra* | (1) | large distribution area in northern lake — NW coast: north of Nkhata Bay to northern end of lake; islands of Likoma and Chisumulu; NE coast: entire coast of Tanzania (Ikombe to Hai Reef at border of Mozambique); partly represented by location variants. |
| *C. axelrodi* | (1) | medium to large distribution area — NW coast: Nkhata Bay to about Lions Cove. |
| *C.* "Black Dorsal" | (1) | very small distribution area — only at Mbenji Island. |
| *C.* "Black Eastern" | (2) | small distribution area — SE coast in the area of Makanjila/Fort Maguire (possibly location variant of *C. afra*). |
| *C.* "Chinyankwazi" | (1) | very small distribution area — found only at the small islands of Chinyankhwazi and Chinyamwezi (SE arm of the lake). |
| *C.* "Jalo" | (2) | very small distribution area — Jalo Reef north of Nkhota Kota. |
| *C.* "Lion" | (1, 2) | medium to large distribution area — NW coast: Chadaga, Lions Cove, Mara Rocks (Usisya). |
| *C.* "Maleri" | (1) | very small distribution area — SE region of Maleri Island. |
| *C.* "Mara" | (2) | found at Mara Rocks (Usisya), probably a location variant of *C. afra*. |
| *C.* "Mbamba" | (1) | large distribution area — NW coast: Nkhata Bay to north end of the lake; islands of Likoma and Chisumulu. |
| *C.* "Mpanga" | (1) | very small distribution area (?) — Mpanga Rocks at Chilumba. |
| *C.* "Ndumbi" | (1) | very small distribution area (?) — Ndumbi Rocks (Likoma). |
| *C.* "Taiwan" | (2) | very small distribution area — Taiwan Reef (north of Chisumulu). |
| *C.* "Yellow Dorsal" | (1) | very small distribution area — only at Mbenji Island. |

(1) = RIBBINK et al. 1983; (2) = KONINGS 1992

# *Cynotilapia afra*  (GÜNTHER 1893)

## Characteristics

Medium-sized Mbuna ca 9 to 11 cm long. Body as a rule is elongate, but variable in this respect, a fact that is probably related to the available food in a certain biotope. Melanin pattern consists of dark to black cross bars on (in males) a light-blue background. The bars appear dependent on mood and are the strongest in dominant males. The width of the bars varies considerably with population. If the bars are very wide (and there is a correspondingly strong formation of black pigmentation in fins and head area), one gets the impression that the specimen in question is completely black and carries white-bluish bars. *C. afra* also exhibits a high degree of variability with respect to the coloration of the dorsal in the male. Even within a population there are occasionally males with white as well as with yellow dorsals (RIBBINK et al. 1983: 235–236). Females and juveniles are grey to brown and exhibit the typical melanin pattern to a lesser degree.

## Distribution

*C. afra* is widely distributed in the northern part of the lake. On the northwest coast (Malawi), this species can be found approximately from Nkhata Bay to the north of Chilumba in all suitable biotopes. Other distribution areas are the islands of Likoma and Chisumulu. On the northeast coast, we also found *C. afra* from the north (Ikombe) all the way to the border of Mozambique (Hai Reef) in nearly every rocky or stony biotope.

## Habitat and feeding

Rocky and stony substrates in shallow water to depths of 40 m form the natural biotopes of *C.*

*afra*. Males hold territories in front of rocks or between stones, which are intensely defended. Females and juveniles are solitary or live in groups which also include non-territorial males, ca 1 m above the bottom. They feed primarily on plankton. If plankton occurs in great abundance, in some locations one may find enormous schools several meters above the rocky bottom in open water. However, territorial males feed more on Aufwuchs (for feeding habits compare with the genus description).

## Similar species

From investigations in Malawi (RIBBINK et al. 1983: 236), it is known that *C. afra* occurs together with *C.* "Mbamba" along the northwest coast and near the islands of Likoma and Chisumulu (sympatric species). *C.* "Mbamba" tends to be higher-backed and prefers deeper water than *C. afra*. Furthermore, *C.* "Mbamba" has a white-to-yellow blaze on its forehead. If one can find and compare both species in one biotope, a distinction between the males is easy, while it is very difficult to differentiate the females of the two species. During our research in Tanzania, we were unable to find *C.* "Mbamba" in any population. Granted, the characteristic feature of *C.* "Mbamba", the bright forehead blaze, is not always clearly formed, while in some populations of *C. afra* the dark pigmentation in the forehead area is only faintly visible. Consequently, one cannot say with certainty that *C.* "Mbamba" is completely absent from the coast of Tanzania. Further investigations are necessary.

## Comments

We compared the Tanzanian populations at Lumbira, Lupingu, Magunga, Cove Mountain,

*Cynotilapia afra* (Magunga)

*Cynotilapia afra* (Ndumbi Reef)

Manda, Ndumbi, Lundu, Njambe, Puulu, Hongi Island, Mbahwa Island, Lundo Island, Luhuchi Rocks, and Mara Rocks (Mbamba Bay), Undu Point, and Hai Reef. The accompanying photographs show the great (geographical) variability of the different populations with respect to coloration of the dominant males. The following compares the coloration of the individual populations from north to south. It should be kept in mind that even within one population large color variations occur.

At Lumbira, *C. afra* exhibits a yellow forehead as well as yellow leading edges of the pelvic fins. The edge of the dorsal is also partly yellow. The yellow pigmentation on the forehead is formed with varying intensities.

The populations of Lupingu, Magunga, Cove Mountain, and Manda have the "standard coloration" (cf. the photographs) with individually differing proportions of yellow in the dorsal.

At Ndumbi Reef, we found very elongate specimens with narrow vertical bars and only few black pigmentations. This population, due to the location of the underwater reef at Ndumbi, which is probably surrounded by wide sandy areas, might be considered isolated.

The coastal regions of Lundu, Njambe, and Hongi Island are again inhabited by "normal" colored *C. afra*.

At Mbahwa Island, one can find specimens with very strong black pigmentation.

South of Mbahwa Island, the populations at Lundo Island, Mara Rocks, and Luhuchi Rocks (both in Mbamba Bay), Undu Point, and Hai Reef do not show any special variations. The robust yellow pigmentation in the dorsals of specimens from Lundo Island and Luhuchi Rocks was, however, conspicuous.

*Cynotilapia afra* (Lumbira)

*Cynotilapia afra* (Lupingu)

*Cynotilapia afra* (Hongi Island)

*Cynotilapia afra* (Mbahwa Island)

*Cynotilapia afra* (Mara Rocks, Mbamba Bay)

*Cynotilapia afra* (Luhuchi Rocks, Mbamba Bay)

*Cynotilapia afra* (Undu Point)

*Cynotilapia afra* (Hai Reef)

167

# *Cynotilapia* "Lion"

### Name

The tentative name refers to the location of discovery, Lions Cove (north of Nkhata Bay) on the northwest coast (RIBBINK et al. 1983: 237). Another term used for the Tanzanian population, is *C.* "Purple/Yellow" (DeMASON 1993a).

### Characteristics

Medium-sized cichlid which under natural conditions reaches a total length of ca 8 to 10 cm. Depending on location, this species is more or less elongate. The head and back are yellow, the flanks bluish (depending on mood). The melanin pattern consists of dark vertical bars. The dorsal shows a strongly marked black submarginal band that is individually very variable. The population of Lions Cove does not exhibit a continuous black submarginal band, but pigment spots which, as an extension of the vertical bars, jut out into the dorsal. The females are yellow-brownish with a fainter melanin pattern.

### Distribution

Found on the northwest coast in the region of Chadaga, Lions Cove, up to roughly Mara Rocks at Usisya (KONINGS 1992: 98) and along the northeast coast at Cape Kaiser (DeMASON 1993a), Magunga, Manda, and Lundu. The various locations on the northeast coast lie on a coastal strip that is about 70 km long (as the crow flies). Presumably this species is distributed also on the bordering coastline.

### Habitat and feeding

Mixed sand-rock and purely rocky substrates, ranging from shallow water (2 to 3 m) to depths of about 30 m, both on the west and east coasts, form the biotopes of *C.* "Lion". Based on our own observations on the west coast one finds this species more frequently over mixed substrates while the populations living at Magunga, Manda, and Lundu inhabit pure rock or stone substrates. The males defend territories between rocks. Females are mostly encountered solitary, adjacent to the male territories. *C.* "Lion" feeds on plankton and Aufwuchs (see genus description for food sources).

### Similar species

Within the genus *Cynotilapia* the coloration of this species is so characteristic that no confusion is likely to occur. While similarly colored *Pseudotropheus* spp. exist, the latter can be easily distinguished because of their bicuspid teeth; *Cynotilapia* spp. have unicuspid teeth (cf. genus description).

### Comments

In the author's view the color differences between populations on the west and east coasts are only slight and must be considered geographical variants. For this reason the name *C.* "Lion" was used and not the term *C.* "Purple/Yellow" (see under Name). For characterization of different populations, the location should be given in parentheses, e.g., *C.* "Lion" (Magunga).

*Cynotilapia* "Lion" (Magunga)

*Cynotilapia* "Lion" (Lions Cove)

*Cynotilapia* "Lion" (Manda)

*Cynotilapia* "Lion" (north-western shore, aquarium photo)

*Cynotilapia* "Lion" (Lundu)

169

The characteristic feature of the *Gephyrochromis* spp., which attain a total length of ca 10 to 12 cm, is the peculiar dentition which consists of thin, long-stemmed, and very tightly packed teeth. At present, two species have been described scientifically: *G. lawsi* and *G. moorii*. Another, so far undescribed species is *G.* "Zebroides" from the southeast coast (region north of Makanjila/Fort Maguire; KONINGS 1992: 269). The preferred biotope is the intermediate (rock/sand) zone. Aufwuchs and small invertebrates appear to be the chief source of food (cf. FRYER 1957).

The first-named species was described in 1957 and is known from the northwest coast north of Nkhata Bay (the type specimens stem from Nkhata Bay and Florence Bay, Chilumba; FRYER 1957).

*G. moorii* was described as early as 1901 (BOULENGER 1901: 4), yet the identity of this species awaits final clarification. While cichlids were exported some time ago for which the description of *G. moorii* fits, the place of discovery of these individuals was not documented reliably. The only type specimen of this species at that time was caught at the "northern end" of the lake. TREWAVAS found more individuals of this species at Karonga, also on the northwest coast (TREWAVAS 1946: 244).

(Note: KONINGS (1992: 268) mentions that he observed *G. moorii* in the wild and even describes characteristics of the cichlid species observed by him, but his illustrations are of aquarium specimens and he reports that *G. moorii* (i.e., the species observed by him) only occurred south of Nkhata Bay. Consequently, either the specimens mentioned by KONINGS are not *G. moorii* or the data on the place of discovery are incorrect.)

In Tanzania, we found another *Gephyrochromis* sp. which is conspicuous due to its yellow pigmentation (*G.* "Yellow"). Again, due to the unanswered questions described above, it cannot be determined at this point whether in *G.* "Yellow" we are dealing with a new species or merely with a geographical race (see below).

*Gephyrochromis* cf. *moorii* (aquarium photo)

*Gephyrochromis* cf. *moorii*, mouthbrooding female; note the long slender and narrowly spaced teeth (aquarium photo).

# Gephyrochromis "Yellow"

### Name

The tentative name refers to the intensive yellow coloration on the cheek, chest, and back areas of this species.

### Characteristics

See Name. Also conspicuous is the single large egg spot in the anal fin of the male. Females are brown to grey. Total length ca 10 to 12 cm.

### Distribution

Found in Mbamba Bay. Probably wide distribution.

### Habitat and feeding

The population observed by us lived above a sandy bottom near the pontoon sunk directly in front of the beach at Mbamba Bay, at a depth of about 6 to 8 m. It was a small group of about ten specimens which lingered near the pontoon. Within the group there was only one male in breeding colors. While the male occasionally chased after other members in the group, we were not able to determine whether he defended a territory in doing so. The individuals obtained food from the sandy substrate so that we must assume that small invertebrates comprise the main food source.

### Similar species

G. "Yellow" is similar to G. lawsi as far as body shape is concerned. Possibly, G. "Yellow" might be classified as a geographical color variant of G. lawsi. Further investigations are needed (cf. genus description).

Gephyrochromis "Yellow" (Pontoon, Mbamba Bay)

# The genus *Labeotropheus*

Two species are listed in the genus *Labeotropheus*: *L. fuelleborni* and *L. trewavasae*. The characteristic feature of both *Labeotropheus* spp. is the unique form of the mouth, which is extremely underslung. Here, the upper portion of the snout looks like a nose that has been pulled over the mouth. Due to this mouth position, *Labeotropheus* spp. are capable of grazing on horizontal surfaces while remaining in a normal swimming position.

L. *fuelleborni* and *L. trewavasae* are only distinguished by their relative body depth. *L. fuelleborni* is high-backed, while *L. trewavasae* is substantially more elongate. Since relative body depth, as in the other Mbunas, is influenced by nutrition, it is sometimes difficult to classify individuals in either one or the other species. This is particularly true for aquarium specimens, which as a rule receive abundant food. In some cases, the question arises whether we are dealing with a slender *L. fuelleborni* or with a fattened-up *L. trewavasae*. Contrastingly, in the wild, it is usually possible to make this distinction immediately, if one can directly compare specimens of both species. Also *L. trewavasae* inhabits deeper water (usually deeper than 5 m) while *L. fuelleborni* is a typical inhabitant of shallow water, who preferably lives close to rocks directly below the water surface.

## *Labeotropheus fuelleborni*

### Characteristics

Large, high-backed Mbuna that reaches a total length of over 15 cm. Typical characteristic, in connection with the relatively deep body, is the extremely underslung mouth (cf. genus description). A melanin pattern is only hinted at and consists of dark vertical bars. *L. fuelleborni* is a polymorphous species. In addition to the normal blue color there is an O as well as an OB morph in both sexes. Furthermore, numerous geographical color variants exist (see Comments). The females of the normal variety are usually an inconspicuous grey to brownish color.

### Distribution

*L. fuelleborni* is one of the most widely distributed Mbunas. Along the coastal regions of Malawi this species was found on nearly every rocky or stony coastline (RIBBINK et al. 1983: 237). In Tanzania, we also found this species on nearly every coast. This species probably has lake-wide distribution.

### Habitat and feeding

Rocky zone in shallow water to a depth of about 5 m is the preferred biotope of this species. Rarely encountered at greater depths. *L. fuelleborni* feeds primarily on Aufwuchs, which is virtually scraped off the rock surface. The underslung mouth enables this species to reach rock surfaces that are submerged only a few centimeters in water (which are precisely the surfaces with the most luxurious Aufwuchs since here the light intensity is greatest) in a horizontal body position. Males are territorial; females, as a rule, are solitary.

## Similar species

Because of the typical mouth, this species is very distinct from cichlids in other genera. To differentiate this species from *L. trewavasae*, see the genus description.

## Comments

Several geographical color variants are known. The overall blue form is considered the normal variety (all data refer to the male sex), which on the coast of Malawi lives primarily in the southern regions up to about Nkhata Bay and at Likoma and Chisumulu. Variations between the southern populations pertain primarily to the intensity of the blue coloration and the coloration of the fins, particularly the dorsal fin (yellow, reddish, partially with black pigmentation). Several *L. fuelleborni* populations from the northwest coast north of Nkhata Bay show a yellowish belly and flank coloration, while the back remains blue. Especially beautiful specimens of this color form live along the offshore reefs and islands of the village of Chilumba.

In Tanzania, at all places where we found this species, we were able to document the completely blue form. Only at Ngkuyo Island (Mbamba Bay) did we discover blue specimens with orange dorsals.

*Labeotropheus fuelleborni* (Cove Mountain)

# *Labeotropheus trewavasae*

## Characteristics

Elongated cichlid with extremely underslung mouth. At a total length of ca 12 to 13 cm it remains smaller than *L. fuelleborni*. The melanin pattern, consisting of dark vertical bars, is usually only faint. The basic coloration of males is blue, that of females brownish to grey. *L. trewavasae* is a polymorphous species which forms OB and O morphs in both sexes. The proportion of O to OB morphs seems to fluctuate with the population; i.e., at certain spots one finds the O morphs particularly often (for example, at Thumbi West Island in the south of the lake), while the same morph is practically nonexistent at other locations. *L. trewavasae* has formed several geographical color variants (cf. Comments).

## Distribution

Distributed along most coastal sections of Malawi (cf. RIBBINK et al. 1983: 239–240). In Tanzania, we were also able to observe *L. trewavasae* in many coastal regions (Manda, Pombo Reef, Tumbi, Puulu, Puulu Island, Hongi Island, Ngkuyo Island at Mbamba Bay). Thus it can be assumed that *L. trewavasae* is distributed throughout the entire lake. However, in some locations in the regions investigated in Malawi, *L. trewavasae* was not detectable (for example, at Chisumulu; cf. the above-mentioned authors).

## Habitat and feeding

In contrast to *L. fuelleborni*, *L. trewavasae* does not prefer shallow water but inhabits the rocky zone at 5 m or deeper. On the Tanzanian coast, we found this species primarily between 10 and 25 m, rarely in deeper water. The males are mostly territorial, but not very aggressively so. Females and subadults are solitary or live in small groups. *L. trewavasae* feeds mostly on Aufwuchs.

## Similar species

Owing to the underslung, genus-typical shape of the mouth, the only other species with which it might be confused with is *L. fuelleborni*, though the latter, as a rule, is much higher-backed (cf. genus description).

## Comments

Similar to *L. fuelleborni*, *L. trewavasae* has also formed geographical color races. Along the southern west coast up to approximately Nkhata Bay, all populations are blue and vary primarily only with respect to the coloration of the dorsal (pertaining to males). Thus the populations of Thumbi West Island and Zimbawe Rock (both locations at Cape Maclear) exhibit a red-orange dorsal fin. The populations of Boadzulu Island, Maleri Island, and Namalenji Island also exhibit an orange dorsal fin. On the west coast north of Nkhata Bay, a yellow-brown broad longitudinal band is formed with varying intensity on the flanks (for example, at Nkhata Bay) or the entire upper body half is yellowish-brown (for example, at Chitendi Island, Chilumba). This latter coloration is also exhibited by the population north of Makanjila (southeast coast, Malawi).

On the Tanzanian coast all of these populations, with the exception of the one at Ngkuyo Island, showed the same coloration as that found on the northeast coast. The Ngkuyo Island population is colored completely differently: the entire body is deep-blue while the dorsal exhibits a broad black longitudinal band. Anal and caudal fin are also blackish. This color variant had not been known until now. Interestingly enough, at the small island of Chinyankhwazi in the southeast of the lake a *L. fuelleborni* population exists that is colored analogously.

*Labeotropheus trewavasae*, female (Ngkuyo Island, Mbamba Bay)

*Labeotropheus trewavasae* (Ngkuyo Island, Mbamba Bay)

*Labeotropheus trewavasae* (Puulu Island)

*Labeotropheus trewavasae* (Hongi Island)

*Labeotropheus trewavasae* (Manda)

*Labeotropheus trewavasae*, OB females (Pombo Reef)

176

# The genus *Labidochromis*

*Labidochromis* species are considered the dwarf cichlids of Lake Malawi. Rarely do they reach a total length of 10 cm. Under natural conditions most species grow to a size of 7 to 8 cm, but in the aquarium, with an abundant food supply, nearly all species have the capacity to grow larger. This, by the way, is true for nearly all Mbunas.

Genus-typical are the forward-pointing teeth (unicuspid or bicuspid) in connection with the behavior during foraging. While *Labidochromis* spp. feed on Aufwuchs, they do not scrape off the algal mat but rather search specifically for small invertebrates which are collected more or less individually. Some species are non-territorial even in the male sex. In small troops that may contain both sexes, *Labido-chromis* spp. roam through the mostly stony biotopes and forage. Aufwuchs is examined from a slightly bent-downward body position until prey is discovered. This gives way to the impression that *Labidochromis* spp. only pluck at the algal mat. This feeding behavior is characteristic so that it is relatively easy to recognize these species in the wild.

From the coast of Malawi 17 species have been described scientifically (for a survey cf. LEWIS 1982; RIBBINK et al. 1983: 229). A few other species are known under working or trade names.

In Tanzania, there live at least eight as yet undescribed species and a further species, *L. maculicauda* which also occurs along the northwest coast.

## *Labidochromis* "Black Dorsal"

### Name

The name refers to the broad black band in the dorsal, which is present in both sexes.

### Characteristics

Relatively large *Labidochromis*, which may reach an overall length of 9 to 11 cm, though most specimens are smaller. Front teeth are unicuspid. Males have black vertical bars that are wide on top, but often get narrower ventrally. The bars may continue into the dorsal so that the anterior region of the dorsal (except for the white edge) appears to be completely black. Egg spots are comparatively faint even in males. Females exhibit a primarily white basic coloration with only the suggestion of vertical bars.

### Distribution

We were able to find specimens of this species at Lundo Island and Puulu Island. *L.* "Black Dorsal" probably also inhabits the coastal regions between the locations mentioned. At Lundo Island, we encountered *L.* "Black Dorsal" relatively frequently on the shallow eastern shore of the island. In contrast, only a few specimens were seen at Puulu Island.

**Habitat and feeding**

Rocky and intermediate substrates are among the biotopes of this species. *L.* "Black Dorsal" lives primarily in shallow water from 5 to 10 m (at Lundo Island), but also at depths to at least 35 m (Puulu Island). This species is probably not or at most weakly territorial; even males in full breeding coloration do not defend territories. Based on the author's aquarium observations, however, conspecific males behave aggressively.

According to our underwater observations, *L.* "Black Dorsal" lives on micro-organisms which are purposefully plucked from the Aufwuchs.

**Similar species**

A species similar in color, yet easy to distinguish, is known from the island of Chisumulu: *L. chisumulae*. The author has raised several specimens of both species in the aquarium. Neither the males nor the females of the different species were paid much attention, in comparison to other aquarium inhabitants. This suggests that we are not concerned with location variants of one species. Also, *L. chisumulae* is clearly smaller than *L.* "Black Dorsal".

*L. caeruleus*, a species that occurs along the northwest coast, sports an overall white coloration in both sexes and, depending on location, also shows a black lateral band in the dorsal. The females of both species are thus very similar.

**Comments**

*L.* "Black Dorsal" has been imported already in small numbers to Germany.

*Labidochromis* "Black Dorsal", female (Puulu Island)

*Labidochromis* "Black Dorsal" (Lundo Island)

# *Labidochromis* "Blue/White"

**Name**

The name refers to the different coloration of the sexes.

**Characteristics**

Medium-large Mbuna of ca 7 to 9 cm, with a rounded head line. Males are an overall light-blue with a white edge to the dorsal. The melanin pattern consists of the suggestion of vertical bars, depending on mood. Anal and pelvic fins exhibit deposits of black pigment. Females are of a uniform white and carry only weakly formed egg spots in the anal fin.

**Distribution**

We found this species at Magunga, along the rocky coasts directly north of Manda and at Tumbi Reef. Probably widely distributed, but nowhere frequent. At the above-mentioned lo-cations too, this species was only rarely encountered.

**Habitat and feeding**

Rocky substrates at depths ranging from ca 10 to 30 m. Large males hold territories between stone crevices or caves, though these territories are defended comparatively weakly against intruders. Females were encountered only in a solitary state. Like other *Labidochromis*, *L.* "Blue/White" feeds on micro-organisms that live in the Aufwuchs (cf. genus description).

**Similar species**

Three more or less uniformly white species are known from Malawi: *L. caeruleus, L. pallidus,* and *L. mylodon.* In all three species the males are colored white to a faint bluish color, so that mix-ups should only occur with the females.

*Labidochromis* "Blue/White", female (Tumbi Reef)

*Labidochromis* "Blue/White" (Tumbi Reef)

# *Labidochromis* "Blunt Nose"

### Name

This tentative appellation was selected because of the conspicuously blunt nose.

### Characteristics

The nose, slightly pushed over the upper jaw, results in the appearance typical for this species. Total length about 8 to 9 cm. Males are elongate, with light-blue body and dark-blue vertical bars. Dorsal dark-blue with a dark band, which is a continuation of the dark-blue bars into the dorsal. Anal fin in the anterior lower region also dark-blue. Females are grey to brown with a similar melanin pattern.

### Distribution

So far discovered only along the rocky coast north of Manda at Cove Mountain, but it is probably more widespread, at least in the region of the Livingstone Mountains.

### Habitat and feeding

Rocky and stony substrates in shallow water of about 3 to 10 m. Males defend small territories. This is a shy species, of which we observed only few specimens. According to our underwater observations Aufwuchs and food particles are picked up from the substrate.

### Comments

Due to its head shape this species is not to be considered a typical *Labidochromis*. It is possible that more detailed investigations will reveal that this species should be ordered within another genus.

*Labidochromis* "Blunt Nose" (Cove Mountain)

# Labidochromis "Deep Body"

## Name

The tentative working name refers to the high-backed body.

## Characteristics

Large *Labidochromis* sp. which reaches a total length of about 9 to 10 cm. Strong dark-blue to black pigmentation that is not limited to the barring pattern but is also strongly present in head and lower body. The dorsal has a white edge; the leading edge of the pelvic fin is also white. We did not observe females. In analogy to related species, it can be assumed that the females are colored brown or grey and that they exhibit a fainter barring pattern.

## Distribution

*L.* "Deep Body" lives along the rocky coast north of Manda and also at Pombo Reef. Probably distributed further.

## Habitat and feeding

Species that lives in hiding, of which we saw only a few specimens. Rocky and intermediate substrates appear to form the preferred biotope. We found this cichlid only in shallow water between ca 3 and 10 m. *L.* "Deep Body" feeds on small organisms contained in the Aufwuchs.

## Similar species

*L.* "Deep Body", with respect to coloration, resembles *L. zebroides*, a species that has become known from the tiny island of Masimbwe (at Likoma Island; Lewis 1982: 253). However, *L.* "Deep

Body" is larger and more high-backed and regarding its total appearance clearly distinguishable from this species.

## Comments

The size and high-backed body shape distinguish *L.* "Deep Body" from nearly all other *Labodichromis* spp. Only in terms of feeding is this species comparable with the representatives of this genus.

*Labidochromis* "Deep Body" (Pombo Reef)

# *Labidochromis* "Hongi"

## Name

This cichlid was discovered in 1990 by FLEI-SCHER at the island of Puulu and named *L.* "Puu-lu" (SEEGERS 1991). Later this species was also caught at Hongi Island and propagated in aquaristic circles as *L.* "Hongi" (KNABE 1992). Since the latter name has become well known in the meantime, it will be adopted here.

## Characteristics

Small to medium Mbuna, reaching ca 8 cm total length. Melanin pattern consists of vertical bars, which are primarily formed in the anterior and upper body region. Depending on origin, it shows varying coloration. The most conspicuous form is found in the population of Hongi Island. The males show a completely yellow to orange dorsal. Body coloration is light-blue with contrasting dark vertical bars. Throat and chest area are yellowish. The other populations are colored similarly, but not as intensely. The males of Ngkuyo Island and Undu Point were both rather brownish, had no yellow throat and showed few yellow pigmentation in the dorsal. The females in all populations are colored similarly and sport a brownish basic coloration with only the suggestion of vertical barring.

## Distribution

We found this species at Puulu, Hongi Island, Ngkuyo Island (Mbamba Bay), and Undu Point. KNABE (1992) found *L.* "Hongi" also at Lundo Island. Locations documented so far stretch over a coastline of ca 60 to 70 km. Presumably, *L.* "Hongi" is relatively widespread along the Tanzanian coast.

## Habitat and feeding

*L.* "Hongi" prefers shallow water to a depth of about 10 m. At Puulu Island and Hongi Island large rocks form the underwater landscape. Territorial behavior was particularly easy to observe at Hongi Island since here population density was greatest and several males had staked their territories side by side at depths of ca 5 m. The individual large boulders offered few hiding places. A space at the foot of a rock over sandy bottom or a crevice in a rock served as the center of a territory, so that a region always had to be defended in the horizontal as well as in the vertical plane. Here, even non-conspecific fish were attacked and chased away.

In the rocky littoral of Ngkuyo Island, we observed only few specimens which lived well-hidden between stony crevices. At Undu Point intermediate substrates prevail. Here, *L.* "Hongi" lived between medium-sized stones. We did not see territory-defending males at Undu Point.

The females are solitary and live above or between stones and rocks.

*L.* "Hongi", in true *Labidochromis* fashion, lives chiefly on small invertebrates which are "plucked" from the Aufwuchs.

## Similar species

The characteristic coloration of dominant males is unmistakable.

*Labidochromis* "Hongi" (Hongi Island)

*Labidochromis* "Hongi" (Hongi Island)

*Labidochromis* "Hongi" (Puulu Island)

*Labidochromis* "Hongi" (Undu Point)

*Labidochromis* "Hongi" (aquarium photo)

183

# *Labidochromis* "Luhuchi"

### Name

The name refers to the location of discovery, Luhuchi Rocks.

### Characteristics

Relatively elongate Mbuna which reaches a total length of ca 8 to 9 cm. The basic coloration is light-blue. The melanin pattern consists of dark-blue to black vertical bars. Individually varying strong dark pigmentations are also exhibited in the dorsal.

### Distribution

We found this species only at Luhuchi Rocks (Mbamba Bay).

### Habitat and feeding

The rocky littoral at Luhuchi Rocks consists primarily of massive boulders which reach from the surface to a depth of about 10 to 12 m. The other main feature is a sandy, only moderately sloping bottom (east side of Luhuchi Rocks). *L.* "Luhuchi" was observed by us in shallow water directly beneath the surface down to a depth of ca 10 m. The males appear to be weakly territorial. We were not able to observe females; perhaps they live in hiding. At least at the location of discovery, this is not a frequently occurring species. Based on our observations, *L.* "Luhuchi", like other *Labidochromis* spp., lives primarily on micro-organisms contained in the Aufwuchs (cf. genus description).

### Similar species

*L.* "Luhuchi" shows similarities to *L.* "Red Top Mbamba Bay". The latter species, however, is less elongate and its overall physique seems more robust. *L.* "Red Top Mbamba Bay" can be recognized by its yellow to orange edge of the dorsal.

*Labidochromis* "Luhuchi" (Luhuchi Rocks, Mbamba Bay)

*Labidochromis* "Luhuchi" (Luhuchi Rocks, Mbamba Bay)

184

# *Labidochromis maculicauda* LEWIS **1982**

## Characteristics

Small, elongate Mbuna. Overall length up to ca 9 cm. Basic body coloration grey-bluish to brownish in the males, grey to beige or yellow to orange for females. Particularly in females and juveniles the basic coloration is determined by numerous horizontal beige-yellowish to orange rows of dots. Melanin pattern variable. Frequently, vertical bars are formed. Depending on the individual, sometimes a dark central lateral as well as a second lateral band are formed in the upper body half, creating a chessboard-like pattern. Both lateral bands may be dissolved into dots. Regarding the basic body coloration and the pattern, a large range of variability exists.

## Distribution

Widely distributed along the northwest and northeast coast. LEWIS (1982) caught *L. maculicauda* at Nkhata Bay and Chilumba (northwest coast). RIBBINK et al. (1983: 233) were able to document this species along the northwest coast in numerous places between the above-mentioned locations. Along the northeast coast, we found *L. maculicauda* at nearly every coastal segment we chose for diving, so it must be assumed that this species is widely distributed along the Tanzanian coast (locations of discovery: Kirondo, Cove Mountain, Pombo Reef, Lundo Island, Puulu Island, Ngkuyo Island at Mbamba Bay, and Hai Reef).

## Habitat and feeding

Typical inhabitant of shallow water, rarely encountered below 10 m. The preferred biotope is a stony or rocky substrate, but intermediate substrates are also colonized. *L. maculicauda* is not territory-forming, not even the males, it lives in small groups of about three to five individuals, rarely solitary. These troops are not territorial, but roam slowly over the lake bottom, searching the Aufwuchs for food. Like other representatives of this genus, *L. maculicauda* feeds mainly on small invertebrates that live in the Aufwuchs.

*Labidochromis maculicauda,* female
(Cove Mountain)

*Labidochromis maculicauda,* male and female
(Kirondo)

## Similar species

From the island of Chisumulu, *L. flavigulis* and *L. strigatus* have become known. (These species have been documented also from Likoma. It is speculated, however, that these are "artificial" populations which were unintentionally abandoned by catchers of ornamental fish; cf. RIBBINK et al. 1983: 232–233.) Both species show a strong resemblance to *L. maculicauda*. In particular, older aquarium specimens are very hard to distinguish. At the present time it cannot be ruled out that one of these species is a geographical subspecies of *L. maculicauda*, at least until more studies on the variability of this species are available.

Another species that must be mentioned in this context is *L. textilis*. In the past, specimens by this name have been imported frequently in aquaristic circles. It is, however, doubtful whether these specimens had been identified correctly and so were actually conspecific with *L. textilis*. The first description of *L. textilis* was based on specimens which, as found out later, belonged to different species. A revision of these type specimens yielded the result that the holotype (a definitive specimen of a species description) represents a new species (LEWIS 1982: 202–203). The specific rank of *L. textilis* is thus verified. The live coloration of *L. textilis* is not known. The location of discovery is presumably the coast of Mozambique opposite Likoma. A crucial characteristic of *L. textilis* is the robust and slightly projecting lower jaw while in *L. maculicauda* the lower jaw is of the same length or shorter than the upper jaw.

Seegers reported in 1991 on *Labidochromis* spp. from Tanzania and mentioned (among others) *L.* "Matema" and *L.* "Lundo" from the corresponding locations of discovery. Seegers pointed out the resemblance of *L.* "Matema" to *L. maculicauda*. Taking into consideration the variability of *L. maculicauda*, perhaps both species are really *L. maculicauda*.

## Comments

A strong sexual dichromatism is not exhibited by *L. maculicauda*. Younger females often display intensive yellow or orange rows of dots on the scales and are thus easily recognized. Older females are more beige, grey or even bluish. With regard to the formation of egg spots in the anal fin, there are females who have a number comparable to those found in males. In the males, which as a rule are larger than females, the blue or dark colors dominate.

The variability of this species is remarkable. In Nkhata Bay, the author found specimens whose vertical bars were very irregular and sometimes divided. Here the large variability in width does not appear to depend on geographical factors, but within a certain population there evidently exist differently colored specimens with regular and irregular vertical barring.

*Labidochromis maculicauda* (Ngkuyo Island)

*Labidochromis maculicauda* (Lundo Island)

*Labidochromis maculicauda,* female (Hai Reef)

*Labidochromis flavigulis* (Chisumulu Island, aquarium photo)

*Labidochromis maculicauda* (Chirwa Island, Chilumba)

*Labidochromis maculicauda* (Nkhata Bay)

# *Labidochromis* "Perlmutt"

## Name

The species name "Perlmutt" is the trade name of this scientifically still undescribed species and pertains to the "iridescent mother-of-pearl sheen" on the flanks of the males (LEPEL 1993a).

## Characteristics

Small Mbuna reaching a total length of ca 8 to 9 cm. Basic coloration whitish. Melanin pattern consists of broad dark vertical bars. In dominant males the barring is only faintly visible. The background coloration is superimposed by a bluish sheen (cf. the trade name). In the male sex, the dorsal and caudal fins are primarily yellowish.

## Distribution

LEPEL (1993a) mentioned as the location of discovery "near Mbamba Bay". We found a very few specimens at the Mara Rocks offshore of Mbamba Bay.

## Habitat and feeding

The few individuals observed by us, lived in the rocky littoral above large stones or boulders at a depth of 10 to 20 m. Evidently a rare species. We did not observe how they obtained their food. Presumably this species, like other *Labidochromis*, feeds on small invertebrates that live in Aufwuchs.

## Similar species

Other whitish *Labidochromis* spp. from Tanzania are *L.* "Black Dorsal" and *L.* "Blue/White" (cf. the preceding pages). In reference to these species, *L.* "Perlmutt" in the male sex can be recognized by its yellow dorsal and caudal fins, the female sex by its broad dark vertical bars.

*Labidochromis* "Perlmutt", female (aquarium photo)

*Labidochromis* "Perlmutt", male and female (Mara Rocks, Mbamba Bay); photo: Annette Bentler

*Labidochromis* "Perlmutt" (aquarium photo)

*Labidochromis* "Perlmutt", subadult male (aquarium photo)

189

# *Labidochromis* "Red Top Mbamba Bay"

## Name

The tentative name refers to the reddish tips in the dorsal and to the location of discovery.

## Characteristics

A Mbuna with light-blue basic coloration and black vertical bars that reaches a total length of ca 9 cm. The vertical barring is primarily formed in the anterior part of the body. Dorsal with black pigment deposits which continue as an extension of the vertical bars. The lower half of the head and the chest area in dominant males are also black and so are the pelvic fins which have a contrasting white edge. Subdominant males, in contrast, are a washed-out blue-grey. The dorsal sports a broad, white-to-yellowish margin with yellow-orange tips. Also there is individual variation in the intensity of the yellow-orange pigmentations in the posterior part of the dorsal and at the trailing edge of the caudal fin. Some specimens even show yellow pectoral fins. Unfortunately we were unable to observe females.

## Distribution

So far only known from Ngkuyo Island at Mbamba Bay.

## Habitat and feeding

Large stones and rocks form the biotope of *L.* "Red Top Mbamba Bay" at Ngkuyo Island. Not a frequent species, which, in addition, likes to hide. Males observed by us were territorial and at a depth of ca 10 to 15 m defended a shelter or a small stone cave as the center of their territory. *L.* "Red Top Mbamba Bay", like the other *Labidochromis* spp., feeds on small invertebrates which are picked out from the algal mat.

## Similar species

SEEGERS (1991) reported on a *Labidochromis* sp. that he found along the southern and northern coasts of Mbamba Bay and at Ngkuyo Island in the rocky littoral at depths of at least 5 m (*L.* "Mbamba Bay"). According to the photograph included, this cichlid, with great probability, could be conspecific with *L.* "Red Top Mbamba Bay". SEEGERS describes the females as "paler and not so iridescent" and points out that breeding of this species in captivity has already been successful.

*Labidochromis* "Red Top Mbamba Bay" (Ngkuyo Island, Mbamba Bay)

In the past, representatives of the genera *Melanochromis* and *Pseudotropheus* were primarily distinguished on the basis of their pharyngeal teeth: *Melanochromis* tends to exhibit fewer and more robust teeth (TREWAVAS 1935). This purely morphological approach led to a situation where with respect to coloration and body shape quite different species were included within the genus *Melanochromis,* while with regard to body shape and melanin pattern very similar species were ordered into different genera.

The discovery of further species showed that certain species of both genera, owing to their elongated body shape in connection with longitudinal bands, are evidently more closely related than the other genus members which do not have these characteristics (cf. TREWAVAS 1983). Therefore, in anticipation of a revision of the genus, many publications started treating all those species as *Melanochromis* that sported an elongate body and longitudinal bands; for example, *Pseudotropheus auratus* today is listed under the name of *Melanochromis auratus.* It is worth mentioning that in some species the sexes show opposite coloration. In *M. parallelus,* for example, the two longitudinal bands in the male are light-blue, but in the female they are black. Body parts that are colored black in the male are white in the female (reverse pigmentation).

The classification based on body shape and melanin patterning is followed here. Consequently, this means that for species which so far have been classified as *Melanochromis,* but which lack the above-mentioned combination of characteristics, the genus name will be put in quotation marks. In this way, it will be indicated that the species in question will have to be

reordered within another genus in the future or that the genus status is in need of revision (for example,*"Melanochromis" labrosus*).

At present, about 25 *Melanochromis* spp. are known. Apart from *"M" labrosus* we were able to find three species in Tanzania. Of those, *M.* "Northern" is exclusively known in Tanzania.

*Melanochromis melanopterus,* the type species of the genus (aquarium photo)

*"Melanochromis" labrosus* (Lupingu)

# *Melanochromis* "Blue"

## Name

<small>RIBBINK</small> et al. (1983: 207) discovered this cichlid and related the tentative name to the males in full breeding coloration. Most individuals observed in the wild tend to be grey-blue or brownish with a blue sheen.

## Characteristics

Elongate, medium-sized Mbuna with pointed head and large mouth. Total length usually ca 12 cm, rarely larger. Melanin pattern consists of a dark mid-lateral band and another, much fainter lateral band in the upper body half. Both lateral bands are formed relatively weakly. In some specimens, there is a hint of dark vertical bars in the upper body half. Basic coloration of body is brownish, partially brown-yellow. Dominant males are grey or brownish with a blue sheen. In specimens that are very dark all over, the pattern is no longer recognizable. The dorsal, in particular, the edge and posterior area, as well as the edge of the caudal and anal fins, are all yellowish or beige-colored. Occasionally the pectoral fins are also yellow. Egg spots are formed relatively faintly. No clearly marked sexual dichromatism.

## Distribution

*M.* "Blue" has been found along the northwest coast in the region between Nkhata Bay and Chilumba and also at the island of Likoma (RIB-<small>BINK</small> et al. 1983: 207). Based on our own observations, *M.* "Blue" is also distributed along the Tanzanian coast. We observed this species at Nkanda, Njambe, Lundo Island, Ngkuyo Island at Mbamba Bay, Undu Point, and Hai Reef. Altogether a rather rare species; at no location did we find this cichlid in large numbers.

## Habitat and feeding

With regard to biotope, *M.* "Blue" does not appear to be very specialized. We found this cichlid over rocky, stony, and intermediate substrates, sometimes even over a sandy lake bottom near rocks, at a depth of 5 to 30 m. All specimens were not territorial and were also solitary. Even large males in full breeding coloration showed no territorial behavior whatsoever. *M.* "Blue" probably feeds by preying. Numerous times we were able to observe how this species hunted smaller cichlids between stones. This hunting behavior was especially pronounced when a mouthbrooding female had released her fry.

## Similar species

With respect to body shape and coloration this species is very similar to *M.* "Slab", which lives along the middle section of the western coast at the island groups of Mbenji and Maleri. In the female sex, *M.* "Slab" has a light whitish basic coloration with a distinct pattern of lateral bands. The males are brownish and in contrast to *M.* "Blue" exhibit no grey-blue coloration. Another similar species is *M.* "Blotch" from the central eastern coast in the region north of Makanjila/Fort Maguire and of Chisumulu Island (RIBBINK et al. 1983: 204). This cichlid is also a dark brownish color, but it usually has chessboard pattern in the upper body half. It is possible that these three species form a close group.

*Melanochromis* "Blue" (Chirwa Island, Chilumba)

*Melanochromis* "Blue" (Nkanda)

*Melanochromis* "Blue" (Hai Reef)

*Melanochromis* "Blue" (Chitendi Island, Chilumba)

*Melanochromis* "Blotch" (Chisumulu Island)

# *Melanochromis* "Northern"

## Name

This species was discovered by Staeck during a collecting trip in 1976 to the northern end of Lake Malawi in the region of the Livingstone Mountains (Staeck 1976; as *Melanochromis* spec.). This species was first imported in 1992 and labeled *M.* "Northern Blue" (Lepel 1993a). To avoid semantic confusion with *M.* "Blue", only the term *M.* "Northern" will be used.

## Characteristics

Medium to large, elongate Mbuna with pointed head and large mouth. Overall length usually ca 12 cm, occasionally larger than 15 cm. Dominant males are uniformly light-blue with whitish dorsal and anal fins, and without any pattern. Subdominant males show a blue-grey coloration and two black longitudinal bands. Juveniles, subadults and females are whitish with two black longitudinal bands and frequently a black band below the edge of the dorsal (submarginal band). The posterior areas of the caudal and anal fins are yellowish.

## Distribution

*M.* "Northern" can be found with relative frequency in the area of the Livingstone Mountains north of Manda. We found this species quite often at Lumbira, Kirondo, Makonde, Magunga, Cove Mountain, and along the rocky coast bordering in the north. We also observed some specimens at Lundu.

## Habitat and feeding

*M.* "Northern" inhabits rocky as well as intermediate substrates at depths ranging from ca 5 m to 25 m. We found most specimens in water layers deeper than 10 m. As a rule, *M.* "Northern" is solitary and not territorial. Staeck (1976) reported that this species swims around tirelessly, covering quite large distances in the process. We were able to observe how some specimens attempted to prey on smaller Mbunas. *M.* "Northern" probably feeds on small fish and on small invertebrates.

## Similar species

With respect to body shape and coloration, this species resembles *M.* "Lepidophage" from the east coast of Malawi in the region of Makanjila Point (Ribbink et al. 1983: 204). *M.* "Lepidophage" has not been found so far at Likoma or Chisumulu.

## Comments

According to initial aquarium observations, *M.* "Northern" is a comparatively peaceful species (Lepel 1993a). This might be a further indication that there exists a closer relationship to *M.* "Lepidophage" since in that species, too, intraspecific aggression is only weakly exhibited.

*Melanochromis* "Northern" (Makonde)

*Melanochromis* "Northern", female (Kirondo)

*Melanochromis* "Northern" (Kirondo)

*Melanochromis* "Northern", subadult male (Lumbira)

*Melanochromis* "Northern" (Manda)

### Characteristics

Elongate, medium-sized Mbuna which reaches a total length of ca 10 to 12 cm. Head not as pointed as in *M.* "Blue" and *M.* "Northern". Males dark-blue to black with two light-blue to whitish longitudinal bands. The dorsal is black (or sports a broad black band) and has a white edge. Females and juveniles are white to cream-colored with two black longitudinal bands. The dorsal shows another black band.

### Distribution

In Malawi, this species is known from the northwest coast in the area between Nkhata Bay and Chilumba and also from the islands of Likoma and Chisumulu. A population introduced by catchers of ornamental fish also exists at the island of Thumbi West at Cape Maclear (RIBBINK et al. 1983: 205). In Tanzania, we found *M. parallelus* along many coastal sections: Cove Mountain, Tumbi Rock, Puulu, Lundu Island, Luhuchi Rocks at Mbamba Bay, and Hai Reef.

### Habitat and feeding

*M. parallelus* inhabits rocky and intermediate substrates. The preferred depths lie between ca 5 and 15 m. However, this species has also been seen at depths of 40 m (RIBBINK et al. 1983: 206). Most specimens are solitary; only rarely did we find small troops of this species. *M. parallelus* is probably not (or only weakly so) a territory-forming species; even males in full breeding coloration are barely territorial. While *M. parallelus* is widely distributed, it rarely occurs in large numbers; mostly we found only a few solitary individuals during our diving ex-

cursions. *M. parallelus* feeds on micro-organisms which are obtained from the Aufwuchs or from the sandy bottom, and occasionally it will eat plankton. According to RIBBINK et al. (1983: 206) small fish are also eaten.

### Similar species

*M. parallelus* is colored very similarly to *M. vermivorus*, a species that is at home in the southern part of the lake (Mbenji Island to Monkey Bay, and also along some reefs in the southeastern part; cf. RIBBINK et al. 1983: 203). The only difference is that the head of *M. parallelus* is not quite as pointed as that of *M. vermivorus*. Furthermore, *M. vermivorus* does not show a black dorsal or black band in the dorsal, but rather a completely whitish to bluish dorsal. The females of *M. vermivorus* are grey and not white as those of *M. parallelus*.

*Melanochromis parallelus*, subadult male (Lundo Island)

*Melanochromis parallelus* (aquarium photo)

*Melanochromis parallelus*, female (Puulu)

*Melanochromis parallelus* (Luhuchi Rocks, Mbamba Bay)

*Melanochromis parallelus* (Hai Reef)

*Melanochromis vermivorus* (Chinyankhwazi Island)

# The genus *Petrotilapia*

Representatives of the genus *Petrotilapia* are the largest of the Mbunas. Nearly all species grow larger than 15 cm and older males can easily reach 18 cm in total length. The essential characteristic of these species, apart from their size, is the shape of the mouth in connection with the dentition. The thick, slightly pursed lips (due to which members of this genus are also called thick lip cichlids) are covered with tightly packed teeth which, even when the mouth is closed, are always visible. This gives rise to the impression that the mouth, particularly in fully grown specimens, is always open and that, in fact, it cannot be completely closed. A similar mouth structure can be found only as far as it is known, in *P. fainzilberi*. This latter species cannot be confused with the *Petrotilapia* spp. due to its small size and the zebra-like pattern.

The relatively long-stemmed teeth, arranged like a brush, are movable and tricuspid at their upper end. This gives *Petrotilapia* spp. an excellent tool for literally "combing" through the algal mat to find their food. As for most Mbunas, the micro-organisms contained in the Aufwuchs form the mainstay of their nutrition. In the language of the Tonga (= Kitonga), a tribe that lives in Malawi, the thick lip cichlids are also called "Mbuna kumwa", which means "rock hitter" (Fryer & Iles 1972: 70).

As is typical for Mbunas, *Petrotilapia* inhabit rocky or stony substrates. Relatively rarely will one find these species over sandy bottoms interspersed with stones. From observations in the wild, it is known that the males sometimes defend very large territories. For *P. tridentiger* and *P. genalutea* territories with an average size of 22 and 20 m$^2$ were determined

(Marsh et al. 1981). The defense of territory is directed primarily against conspecifics.

Almost all species are morphologically very similar and can best be distinguished by the full breeding coloration of the males. The first species to be described scientifically was *P. tridentiger* in 1935 (Trewavas 1935: 76). This species is very well known among aquarists, if only by name, despite the fact that *P. tridentiger* has hardly been imported so far. *Petrotilapia* spp. imported in the past, as a rule, belonged to other species (Spreinat 1991). Only in 1981 were two more species described scientifically (*P. genalutea* and *P. nigra*) when, owing to observations in the wild, it became evident that the morphologically nearly identical individuals included not just different color forms, but "true", sympatric (living in one location) species (Marsh et al. 1981; Marsh 1983). Ribbink and coworkers, who at the beginning of the 1980s explored vast coastal sections of Malawi, came to the conclusion that in addition to the three scientifically described species there exist 14 more species. The latter, until this day, are only known under so-called working names since no scientific first descriptions have yet been carried out (Ribbink et al. 1983: 209–228). In the more recent literature, Konings (1992: 253, 254) mentions two additional species which, however, are probably mere location variants of the species introduced by Ribbink et al.

Among the closely related members of this species-complex, it is generally very difficult to judge whether a given population is merely a differently colored location variant (geographical form) of an already known species or an independent new species.

Thus it might happen that some of the species introduced by Ribbink et al. represent location variants of already known species or in the future will be summarized as location variants of only a few species. Necessary investigations on the clarification of this conjecture are pending.

In Tanzania, we found *P. tridentiger* and two other new species. These three species live sympatrically along many coastal sections of Tanzania.

*Petrotilapia* spp. are characterized by their brush-like teeth (*Petrotilapia tridentiger* at Boadzulu Island)

A school of *Petrotilapia* "Pointed Head" at Tumbi Rocks

# *Petrotilapia* "Pointed Head"

## Name

This working name was chosen because in comparison to other *Petrotilapia* this species has a pointed head.

## Characteristics

Large Mbuna which reaches an overall length of about 14 to 16 cm. Basic coloration of males is grey-blue to brownish. Head area especially below the eye, the shoulder, and chest are yellowish. The degree of yellow coloration is variable. Sometimes even the flanks exhibit yellow pigmentation. Populations also exist in which the males are primarily yellowish to brownish and show very little blue coloration. Dorsal has black lateral band and white to yellowish tips. In dominant males the melanin pattern is only weakly formed and consists of a few narrow, dark vertical bars. Occasionally a dark mid-lateral band might be visible. The females are beige-colored to (rarely) brownish. The dominant element in the pattern is a broad mid-lateral band which might be dissolved into broad blotches. A second lateral band — running through the middle of the upper body half — is usually only faintly visible. Males that have not as yet developed their full coloration also exhibit the latter pattern.

## Distribution

Probably widely distributed along the Tanzanian coast. We found this species at Ikombe, Nkanda, Lumbira, Kirondo, Lupingu, Pombo Reef, Lundu, Tumbi Rock, Puulu Island, Undu Point, and Hai Reef.

## Habitat and feeding

Stony bottom with large broken rocks seems to be the preferred biotope of this species. We encountered most specimens in shallow water ranging from ca 3 to 8 m. Only rarely did we see *P.* "Pointed Head" below 10 m. The males defend territories whose center is usually located in front of large stones or rocks. Since population density was low, we were unable to estimate the size of their territory. Mostly, the males occupied a circle of about 5 m. The females were solitary or roamed in groups of three to five specimens. At Tumbi Rocks, however, we observed shoals of several hundred individuals, containing mainly females but also some not fully colored males. This location was markedly affected by current. The individuals hovered together in the current and grazed on the Aufwuchs of the surrounding rocks.

## Similar species

As far as the criteria of head shape, coloration, and melanin pattern of the females are concerned, *P.* "Pointed Head", *P.* "Chitande", and *P. genalutea* are very similar. With regard to the distribution area of these three species there is no overlapping. *P.* "Chitande" (Chitendi Island = English Chitande) is distributed around Chilumba, while *P. genalutea* occurs along the west coast from the south (Chemwezi) to Ruarwe in the north and along the east coast around Makanjila (RIBBINK et al. 1983:211, 228). Owing to the great similarity, the three species might represent location variants or geographical races of a widespread species. Detailed further investigations are still pending, so that we have followed the current convention of considering *P.* "Chitande" and *P. genalutea* as two species, and correspondingly *P.* "Pointed Head" as another separate species.

Several populations of *P.* "Tanzania" (see below) in the male sex are colored similarly to *P.* "Pointed Head". Since these two species inhabit the same biotopes over vast coastal regions, there cannot be any doubt that we are faced with two independent species. In the wild, it is quite easy to distinguish the males of both species when a direct comparison is possible.

**Comments**

Based on our observations, the populations north of the Ruhuru estuary appear to exhibit a stronger blue body coloration with yellow in the anterior head region, while populations south of the Ruhuru are generally more yellowish to brownish in color.

*Petrotilapia* "Pointed Head" (Hai Reef)

*Petrotilapia* "Pointed Head" (Pombo Reef)

# Petrotilapia "Tanzania"

## Name

Because of its characteristic melanin pattern and frequent occurrence this species appeared to us to be typical for the Tanzanian coast.

## Characteristics

Depending on location, a medium-sized to large Mbuna (about 13 to 17 cm total length). An essential identification feature of *P.* "Tanzania" is the chessboard-like melanin pattern, consisting of dark vertical bars and lateral bands. The first, more pronounced lateral band is centered on the flanks; the second is centered between the first band and the base of the dorsal. Both lateral bands may be variably dissolved into rows of dots. In the male, this melanin pattern is mostly superimposed by the general pigmentation and therefore only faintly visible. The females are beige-colored to light-brown. As for male coloration, this species is very variable, ranging from nearly black to yellow with different proportions of blue (cf. Comments).

## Distribution

Widespread species along the Tanzanian coast, which we saw in far greater numbers than *P.* "Pointed Head" or *P. tridentiger*. Found at Ikombe, Nkanda, Kironda, Makonde, Lupingu, Magunga, along the rocky coast north of Manda, Ndumbi Reef, Njambe, Tumbi Reef, Puulu Island, Hongi Island, Mara Rocks, and Ngkuyo Island at Mbamba Bay, as well as on the southern coast of Mbamba Bay, and at Hai Reef.

## Habitat and feeding

Rocky and partly intermediate substrates covered with mostly large stones and rocks are in-habited. Regarding the preferred depth we were able to determine that this species, in contrast to the other two species occurring along the Tanzanian coast, is found in deeper waters between ca 10 to 20 m. Which depths are preferred depends essentially on the nature of the substrate at a given depth and on the competition pressure from other species. The males are territorial, but do not appear very aggressive, at least not against other species. Whether they would defend vigorously their territory against conspecific males could not be determined since we rarely had the opportunity to observe two dominant males side by side. Females are solitary or live in small groups of about three to six individuals. *P.* "Tanzania" feeds on Aufwuchs, which is obtained by scraping or combing off the substrate (cf. genus description).

## Similar species

It is obvious that the dark-colored populations of *P.* "Tanzania" strongly resemble other dark-blue or black *Petrotilapia* spp. As the closest relative we might consider *P.* "Black Flank", a species that occurs at Chilumba (Mpanga Rocks, Chitendi Island) on the northwest coast. In the male sex, *P.* "Black Flank" is black or dark purplish. The females, like those of *P.* "Tanzania", show a chessboard-like melanin pattern (RIBBINK et al. 1983: 228). Other dark *Petrotilapia* spp. are *P. nigra* from the southern part of the lake (Monkey Bay and area around Cape Maclear) and *P.* "Gold" which has been found at the small islands of Chinyankhwazi and Chinyamwezi (RIBBINK et al. 1983: 211). In *P.* "Gold" the females are yellow to golden in color. KONINGS, with *P.* "Makanjila Gold", refers to a population that belongs on Malawi's

*Petrotilapia* "Tanzania" (Magunga)

*Petrotilapia* "Tanzania", female (Kirondo)

*Petrotilapia* "Tanzania" (Kirondo)

*Petrotilapia* "Tanzania" (Manda)

*Petrotilapia* "Tanzania" (Ndumbi Reef)

east coast and is very similar to *P.* "Gold". Another black population was discovered at Jaro (Jalo) Reef (middle western coast) and denoted by *P.* "Jalo" (KONINGS 1992: 352, 354). A population that is colored dark-blue to purplish was found at Lions Cove ("Dunkelblauer *Petrotilapia*"; SPREINAT 1991). Based on present knowledge, the above-mentioned dark or black *Petrotilapia* form a circle of closely related species (or subspecies) which have settled on different coastal sections. However, remarkable in this context are the light location forms of *P.* "Tanzania", for example, from Magunga and Hai Reef. These populations fall outside the above argument and point out the necessity of a more differentiated view.

## Comments

As already mentioned, in *P.* "Tanzania" we are faced with a species that is very variable in the male sex with respect to size and coloration. At Kirondo, we observed fully colored and sexually active males that were only about 13 cm in size, while all other populations produced much larger specimens (ca 15 to 16 cm).

Regarding the variation of coloration in the male, it must be mentioned that the northern populations of Ikombe, Nkanda, Kirondo, Makonde, and Lupingu are all nearly black, while at Magunga the males are an intense yellow. A few kilometers further south, along the rocky coasts north of Manda, we again found males that were dark-blue to black. This seems peculiar because between Lupingu and Magunga and between Magunga and Manda the scenery consists exclusively of rocky coasts, with no apparent geographical barriers whatsoever.

South of the Ruhuru's mouth at Ndumbi Reef live dark-blue males which externally do not differ from the Manda population. In the populations of Njambe, Tumbi Reef, Hongi Island, Puulu Island, and Mbamba Bay (southern coast, Ngkuyo Island, Mara Rocks) one finds rather brownish males with differing proportions of yellow pigment. South of Mbamba Bay, at Hai Reef, the males are yellowish with light-blue back and upper head area. The blue coloration varies individually in intensity and also exists on the lower flanks. The dorsal of these specimens is yellowish, without the dark band. In the case of the population at Hai Reef, the author doubts whether this form should be included within the species *P.* "Tanzania", although the melanin pattern of the females speaks for it.

*Petrotilapia* "Tanzania" (Hai Reef)

*Petrotilapia* "Tanzania", female (Ngkuyo Island, Mbamba Bay)

*Petrotilapia* "Tanzania" (Ngkuyo Island, Mbamba Bay)

*Petrotilapia* "Tanzania", female (Hai Reef)

*Petrotilapia* "Tanzania" (Puulu)

# *Petrotilapia tridentiger*

## Characteristics

One of the largest Mbunas, which can reach an overall length of 18 cm. Males are characterized by the light-blue coloration of body and fins. The females are grey-brown to bluish. No distinct sexual dichromatism as in other *Petrotilapia* spp. Melanin pattern hardly exists; there is sometimes a suggestion of dark vertical bars.

## Distribution

Widespread species in Malawi, which has been detected along many coastal regions (southern west coast: from Chemwezi and Boadzulu Island roughly to Cape Maclear; northern west coast: Nkhata Bay to north of Chilumba; does not occur along Malawi's east coast or at the islands of Likoma and Chisumulu; cf. RIBBINK et al. 1983: 210).

In Tanzania, we found this species at Nkanda, Lundu, Puulu Island, and Hongi Island. Many specimens were especially encountered at Hongi Island.

## Habitat and feeding

*P. tridentiger* lives in shallow water of about 3 to 5 m and is rarely found below 10 m. Biotope consists of stony or rocky substrates, whereby large boulders are especially preferred. The males are strictly territorial and defend their domain intensely. Females are solitary, but are sometimes found in small groups. Ribbink et al. (1983: 211) reported that this species also occurs in shoals of up to 200 individuals. Like other species in this genus, *P. tridentiger* feeds primarily on Aufwuchs and the micro-organisms contained in it (cf. genus description).

## Similar species

Owing to the uniform coloration there is hardly any chance of confusing this species with others in the genus. Other blue-colored species such as *P.* "Small Blue" or *P.* "Ruarwe", carry a melanin pattern or yellowish pigmentation in the fin and chest area.

## Comments

Despite its wide distribution, *P. tridentiger* has not formed geographical color forms. This could either mean that evolution took the same course in all populations (or that no visible evolution has taken place) or that the barriers that are usually effective in the case of Mbunas (e.g., sand bays) have no isolating effect and thus a "gene flow" occurs throughout the entire population. The latter case would be unusual, since *P. tridentiger* follows a strongly rock-associated life style. The reasons why some Mbunas form geographical races while other species do not, have been scarcely researched.

*Petrotilapia tridentiger* (Hongi Island)

*Petrotilapia tridentiger*, female (Chilumba)

*Petrotilapia tridentiger* (Hongi Island)

*Petrotilapia tridentiger* (Chilumba)

*Petrotilapia tridentiger* (Boadzulu Island)

Most of the Mbunas are summarized in this genus. Nearly all of the currently known 170 species follow a rock-associated life style and feed primarily on Aufwuchs. The algal mat is practically scraped off the bottom with the bicuspid teeth which by *Pseudotropheus* spp. have been developed especially for this purpose.

As early as 1956 it was pointed out that the definition of the genus *Pseudotropheus* is inadequate (FRYER 1956a: 88). In the course of the rapidly increasing numbers of known species — particularly in the 1970s and 1980s — it became ever more obvious that a revision and subdivision of the genus is necessary. RIBBINK and coworkers, who in 1983 presented the first "preliminary" survey after years of study on the lake, divided the representatives of this genus into three species-groups and three species-complexes (RIBBINK et al. 1983: 157):

P. *elongatus* species-group
P. "Aggressive" species-group
P. "Miscellaneous" species-group
P. *zebra* species-complex
P. *williamsi* species-complex
P. *tropheops* species-complex

In a species-complex — as opposed to a species-group — one starts on the assumption that a monophyletic unit is concerned. This means that all members of a species-complex can be traced directly to one common lineage, i.e., they are all equally closely related to each other (closed descent community or monophylum; for further reading see "The Phylogenetic System" by AX, 1987). In the case of species-groups, not all members are related to an equal-

ly close degree, i.e., within the group under consideration there are several phylogenetic lineages from which the different members have evolved (polyphylum).

Needless to say, the criteria by which to judge whether certain Mbuna spp. present either a monophyletic or polyphyletic unit are hardly comprehensible in an unequivocal manner and as a result varying opinions on the classification of these species abound. A generally valid definition of such criteria does not exist.

Thus, in the opinion of the author, it is not at all clear that the members of the *P. tropheops* species-complex are indeed related to each other to the same close degree (see below).

Generally speaking, the above-described subdivision of the genus *Pseudotropheus* is comprehensible and does indeed facilitate an overview of this heterogeneous "collection genus". For these reasons, in the following text we essentially accept the classification of RIBBINK et al. (1983) and have applied it to the species discovered in Tanzania. Accordingly, representatives of the *P. tropheops*, *P. zebra* species-complex, and the *P. elongatus* species-group are discussed in chapters of their own.

Relatively few species were discovered from other groups or complexes. We were only able to find one representative of the *P. williamsi* species-complex and two species from the *P.* "Aggressive" species-group in Tanzania. For this reason, the species of the remaining species-groups and complexes are not classified further but listed together in alphabetical order.

# *Pseudotropheus* "Aggressive Puulu"

## Name

Both the strict defense of territory by males and the location of discovery are reflected in the name.

## Characteristics

Moderately elongate, medium-sized Mbuna which reaches an overall length of about 12 cm. Head shape rounded with slightly pursed mouth. Melanin pattern only suggested by dark vertical bars. The body's basic coloration in males is blue. The head below the eye, the throat and chest areas are a bold yellow. The posterior parts of the dorsal and the anal and caudal fins are blackish. Females exhibit a grey-brown body coloration and faint vertical bars.

## Distribution

We found a few specimens of this species along the rocky coast north of the village of Puulu.

## Habitat and feeding

The population observed near Puulu lived at a depth of about 5 m. The substrate was closely packed with small and medium-sized stones. The males defended territories of ca 0.8 m (horizontal diameter) against virtually all intruders. The center of the territory was always either a small cave or rocky overhang or similar kind of shelter. The females are solitary and live relatively hidden between stones. Like other species of *Pseudotropheus*, *P.*

"Aggressive Puulu" feeds on Aufwuchs.

## Similar species

As the name indicates, this species should be ordered within the *P.* "Aggressive" species-group established by Ribbink et al. (1983: 190).

As related or similar species from this group we name *P.* "Aggressive Blue" from the southern west coast (Monkey Bay, Cape Maclear, Maleri Islands) and *P.* "Aggressive Grey" from Likoma. The latter species is similar only with respect to the blue-grey basic coloration, as it does not exhibit a yellow but a dark-grey head and chest area instead. Another species in the above group is *P. tursiops*, which we were also able to find in Tanzania.

*Pseudotropheus* "Aggressive Puulu" (Puulu)

209

# *Pseudotropheus* "Black Dorsal Tanzania"

## Name

The name refers to the strongly marked band in the dorsal found in many populations of this species. The addition "Tanzania" is necessary so as to distinguish the species from similar populations in Malawi, called *P.* "Zebra Black Dorsal" or *P.* "Black Dorsal" (see under Similar species).

## Characteristics

Medium-sized species, which, depending on the population, reaches an overall length of ca 12 to 13 cm. Regarding relative body depth and coloration in both sexes, *P.* "Black Dorsal Tanzania" is variable. Older and larger specimens tend to be more high-backed. The basic coloration of males is light-blue with black or dark-blue vertical bars of varying width. The head area below the eye and the chest usually stand out darker. Dorsal, depending on population, has more or less vigorously marked dark band. Basic coloration of females varies from grey-brown to dark-yellow to a robust yellow-orange. The females either show no or only a weakly formed band in the dorsal. The female pattern is only hinted at in dark vertical bars.

## Distribution

Rocky coast north of Manda, Mbahwa Island, Lundo Island, Mbamba Bay, Undu Point, and Hai Reef. We found this species particularly often in the south at Undu Point and Hai Reef.

## Habitat and feeding

*P.* "Black Dorsal Tanzania" prefers intermediate substrates at depths of ca 5 to 15 m, rarely at 20 m. Males are aggressively territorial. Center of the territory (ca 1 m in diameter) is commonly a cave or a cave like shelter between stones. The females swim alone or (rarely) in small groups and linger in the neighborhood of the males' territories. *P.* "Black Dorsal Tanzania" feeds on Aufwuchs and also obtains edibles from sandy substrates.

## Similar species

As already mentioned under Name, similar populations are known from Malawi. As *P.* "Zebra Black Dorsal", RIBBINK et al. (1983: 162) denoted populations that occur among the Maleri island group in the southwest of the lake (Maleri, Nankoma, Nakanthenga). Another population of this species was detected at Chindunga Rocks (Chipoka) (SPREINAT 1988b). Another, closely related population, also living on the southwest coast at the island of Thumbi West (Cape Maclear) was called *P. heteropictus* (RIBBINK et al. 1983: 162). This, however, was a false identification. *P. heteropictus* STAECK 1979 is a completely different cichlid and stems from Chisumulu (*P. heteropictus* was listed as a seemingly new species under the name of *P.* "Newsi"; SPREINAT 1994). These five *P.* "Black Dorsal" populations from the south also prefer intermediate or sediment-rich substrates. The similarity of the populations from Malawi with the widely distant populations in Tanzania is remarkable.

## Comments

Owing to its only moderate similarity with members of the *P. zebra* species-complex, this species is not listed under this species-complex, and the addition "zebra" has been dropped. In the author's opinion, *P.* "Black Dorsal" and *P.*

*Pseudotropheus* "Black Dorsal Tanzania" (Undu Point)

*Pseudotropheus* "Black Dorsal Tanzania", female (Undu Point)

"Black Dorsal Tanzania" should only be classified in the larger group of the true "zebra"-like
fish.

*Pseudotropheus* "Black Dorsal Tanzania" (Lundo
Island)

*Pseudotropheus* "Black Dorsal Tanzania"
(Mbahwa Island)

*Pseudotropheus* "Black Dorsal Tanzania", female
(Lundo Island)

*Pseudotropheus* "Black Dorsal Tanzania" (Lundo
Island)

*Pseudotropheus* "Black Dorsal Tanzania", female
(Hai Reef)

*Pseudotropheus* "Black Dorsal Tanzania" (Hai Reef)

*Pseudotropheus* "Black Dorsal Tanzania", females (Hai Reef)

*Pseudotropheus* "Black Dorsal", female (Maleri Island)

*Pseudotropheus* "Black Dorsal" (Nakanthenga Island)

*Pseudotropheus* "Black Dorsal", female (Thumbi West Island, Cape Maclear)

*Pseudotropheus* "Black Dorsal" (Thumbi West Island, Cape Maclear)

213

# *Pseudotropheus* "Broad Bar"

**Name**

The name refers to the broad dark vertical bars.

**Characteristics**

Medium-sized, relatively high-backed Mbuna, which usually reaches an overall length of ca 10 to 13 cm. Typical characteristics are the broad dark vertical bars, five of which are located below the dorsal. These bars extend partially into the dorsal fin. The basic coloration of the body is silvery-blue (males) or silvery-grey (females). No marked sexual dichromatism. Males have bold egg spots in the anal fin, whereas females carry no or only weakly defined egg spots.

**Distribution**

Found at Nkanda, Lupingu, Magunga, and Lundu. Probably widely distributed. Nowhere did we find this species in large numbers.

**Habitat and feeding**

*P.* "Broad Bar" lives over rocky or intermediate substrates in deep water. We found most specimens at depths of 30 to 40 m. It is generally a rather rare species. Territorial behavior was not observed. As far as Mbuna are concerned, *P.* "Broad Bar" has an unusual life style. Bonding with the substrate is only weakly formed. Instead, as a rule, the individuals swim 1 to 2 m above the bottom and are not territorial. As soon as something of interest has been discovered, *P.* "Broad Bar" zooms in on it purposefully. Occasionally, we had to chase this species away from the camera in order to keep the necessary distance for photographing, since the reflecting Plexiglas housing of the camera was particular-

ly examined in detail. We cannot report observations on feeding habits. Presumably *P.* "Broad Bar" is a comparatively unspecialized omnivore.

**Similar species**

A high-backed body in combination with broad vertical bars is rare within the group of Mbunas. Older males of *P. crabro* also show broad vertical bars, but this species has a yellowish brown basic coloration and is not as high-backed. In the wild, this species can not be easily confused with other Mbunas.

**Comments**

Taking into consideration the atypical, i.e., for Mbunas, fairly unspecialized life style and the absence of sexual dichromatism, one is led to speculate that *P.* "Broad Bar" is a Mbuna that has remained more original and probably closer to a (previous) Mbuna lineage than the highly developed specialists in this group.

Rocky shore south of Lundu

*Pseudotropheus* "Broad Bar" (Lundu)

*Pseudotropheus* "Broad Bar", female (Lundu)

215

# Pseudotropheus "Daktari"

## Name

"Daktari" is a trade name for this species (BENTLER 1993) which makes no reference to any quality of the fish itself (in Kiswahili Daktari means doctor; perhaps the reference is to an African physician who helped the catchers who discovered this species). The trade name was adopted by us. Another name is *P.* "Yellow Acei" (DeMASON 1994a).

## Characteristics

Medium-sized, elongate Mbuna which under natural conditions reaches an overall length of ca 10 cm. The females are a little smaller. Dominant males are lemon yellow and sport black edges in the caudal fin. Occasionally the anal fin also has deposits of blackish pigments. The females are of a monochrome brownish color and exhibit the black edges of the caudal fin in a fainter form. Evidently there are also some females that are colored yellow. Occasionally, a melanin pattern of faint vertical bars is present.

## Distribution

Locations of discovery that are known so far are Hai Reef on the border of Mozambique and a few kilometers further north on the rocky reef at Undu Point. At Undu Point, we could only find few specimens of this species. On Hai Reef, *P.* "Daktari" is one of the most frequent Mbunas and occurs in large numbers.

## Habitat and feeding

*P.* "Daktari" prefers intermediate zones of sand/stone or sand/rock substrates in shallow water of ca 3 to 4 m to depths of about 15 m. Sexual-

ly mature males are territorial. The territory is usually situated against a stone in front of which a small depression has been constructed. The size of the territory is about 0.5 m$^2$ (0.8 × 0.8 m). Females and juveniles live in the adjacent areas and do not appear to be territorial. *P.* "Daktari", as a rule, feeds on Aufwuchs, which is scraped off rocks and stones. We could also observe that this species hovers in extended schools in open water about 1 to 2 m above the lake bottom, feeding on plankton if carried by the current. Provided there is plankton, the males will leave their territory temporarily and join these schools.

## Similar species

*P.* "Lime", *P. lombardoi*, and *P. barlowi* also exhibit yellow coloration in the male sex. The latter two species are, however, higher-backed so that there is hardly any danger of confusion. *P.* "Lime" might be a closely related species.

## Comments

Lake Malawi cichlids in the male sex are commonly colored blue, green or black, i.e., show cool hues. The females, in contrast, are colored brown, yellow or reddish, and exhibit warm colors. In very few cases are males colored yellow or red and the females are blue (for example, in *P. lombardoi*, a species in which the females have blue bars. Only old females of *P. lombardoi* may become yellow).

*Pseudotropheus* "Daktari" (Hai Reef)

*Pseudotropheus* "Daktari", female (Hai Reef)

*Pseudotropheus* "Daktari" (Hai Reef)

*Pseudotropheus* "Daktari", courting male (Hai Reef)

*Pseudotropheus* "Daktari" (Hai Reef)

# *Pseudotropheus demasoni*

## Characteristics

Small Mbuna, which can reach a total length of ca 6 to 8 cm. Males and females have the same coloration. The basic coloration of the body is blue to light blue. The melanin pattern consists of vertical bars ranging from dark-blue to black, which in some specimens are distributed irregularly. The dorsal fin, as a rule, is black with white edging. In some specimens, the dorsal sports a broad black band with black spots, which are an extension of the black barring into the dorsal fin. The tail fin is black with elongated light-blue blotches of color and a white edging. The anal and pelvic fins are also black, with white margin or edges.

## Distribution

Pombo Reef and Ndumbi Reef were the only locations in which we were able to observe this species.

## Habitat and feeding

*P. demasoni*, at the locations mentioned, inhabits intermediate, stony, and rocky substrates in shallow water at depths of ca 2 to 8 m. Most specimens observed by us were solitary and in a given area were mostly loyal to one site. However, this territory was not defended against other fish. We also observed that the territory was sometimes abandoned. In some places, we found several specimens together. Intraspecies aggression appears to be quite weak; most of the fish behaved rather peacefully. *P. demasoni* feeds on Aufwuchs. Remarkably enough, despite its conspicuous coloring and its small size, this species moves quite openly over the substrate and makes no attempt to hide. Yet, this small species is not a fast swimmer and might even be described as placid. *P. demasoni* is not a common cichlid, but stands out among all the others and thus is immediately noticed.

## Similar species

The slight body size in connection with the characteristic coloring and behavior are unmistakable.

## Comments

This species was discovered by us first at Pombo Reef and later at Ndumbi Reef. KONINGS, who went diving after us in this coastal strip, caught some specimens at Pombo Reef and dedicated their description to Laif DeMASON, so that a valid name became available in a very brief time.

We found several juveniles, with an estimated overall length of about 2 to 3 cm. These had the same coloration as fully grown and sexually active specimens. We also observed males who were involved in intense courtship of equally colored but somewhat smaller specimens. Consequently, we are faced with a species in which males and females have identical coloration. This is remarkable insofar as the vast majority of Mbunas exhibits a distinct sexual dichromatism.

*Pseudotropheus demasoni* (Pombo Reef)

*Pseudotropheus demasoni*, juvenile ca. 3 cm long
(Pombo Reef)

*Pseudotropheus demasoni* (Pombo Reef)

*Pseudotropheus demasoni* (Pombo Reef)

*Pseudotropheus demasoni* (Pombo Reef)

219

# *Pseudotropheus* "Dolphin"

## Name

The dolphin-like rounded anterior head was the designating feature for this species.

## Characteristics

Medium-large to large, moderately high-backed Mbuna. Total length ca 12 to 14 cm. Rounded anterior head with slightly protruding mouth. Basic coloration light-blue. Numerous broad black vertical bars, so that the basic coloration on the flanks appears to stand out as narrow light stripes. Head area and pelvic fins are deep black. Dorsal sometimes with black band, or sometimes completely black with contrasting white edge. Anal and caudal fins also have black pigmentation. Males carry several small egg spots in the anal fin. Females are colored similar to males, but overall more greyish to dark.

## Distribution

Found at Tumbi Rocks and along the rocky coast north of Puulu. It is possible that this species is also distributed along the bordering coastal sections.

## Habitat and feeding

At the locations cited above, this species lived at depths of ca 5 to 10 m over rocky substrates. The males are very territorial and defend their domain intensely. Females appear to be solitary, but this is not entirely certain as we saw only a few specimens. Based on our observations, *P.* "Dolphin" feeds primarily on Aufwuchs.

## Similar species

Owing to its size, head shape, and the characteristic coloration, this species is very conspicuous. As a comparable species we mention, with restrictions, *P.* "Chinyankwazi" from the island of the same name from the southeastern arm of the lake (RIBBINK et al. 1983: 195). This species exhibits a similar coloration, but not the typical head shape of *P.* "Dolphin".

*Pseudotropheus* "Dolphin" (Puulu)

*Pseudotropheus* "Dolphin" (Tumbi Rocks)

*Pseudotropheus* "Dolphin" (Puulu)

*Pseudotropheus* "Dolphin" (Tumbi Rocks)

221

# Pseudotropheus "Msobo"

## Name

This species has been known in aquarist circles since the beginning of the 1990s under this trade name (SPREINAT 1993a).

## Characteristics

Medium-sized Mbuna with moderately elongate, robust body shape. Total length is mostly 9 to 10 cm. Forehead line, particularly in older individuals, slightly convex and with small indentation above the mouth, i.e., slightly protruding snout. Melanin pattern and coloration are extremely variable, depending on population. Males are generally light-blue to black with differing patterns. Females and juveniles are grey-yellowish to an intense orange, again depending on population, and have no pattern whatsoever (very rarely can one see the suggestion of vertical bars in females). The geographical variation is described under Comments.

## Distribution

We were able to observe P. "Msobo" between Magunga and Lundo Island along several sections of the coast (Magunga, Cove Mountain, rocky coast north of Manda, Ndumbi Reef, Pombo Reef, Lundu, Njambe, Tumbi Rocks, Tumbi Reef, rocky coast north of Puulu, Puulu Island, Mbahwa Island, and Lundo Island). According to reports by the ornamental fish catchers of E. Johansen, Mbeya, this species also occurs north of Magunga at Cape Kaiser. South of Lundo Island, we could find this species neither at Mbamba Bay and Undu Point nor at Hai Reef.

## Habitat and feeding

Depending on population, rocky, stony, and partly intermediate substrates at a depth of ca 5 to 30 m form the biotope of P. "Msobo".

At Magunga, for example, we found a very high population density in 5 to 10 m over a stony substrate. In shallow water we observed shoals of juveniles. At Tumbi Rocks, this species was also very numerous, at depths of ca 5 to 15 m. Here the substrate consisted of larger stones and rocks. A few hundred meters further south, at Tumbi Reef, we found a few P. "Msobo" in deep water of ca 25 to 30 m over intermediate substrates. In the rocky littoral of the island of Mbahwa we observed the highest density in 15 to 20 m, although the shore of this island, from the surface to the base area, uniformly consists of large rocks. It is possible that competition from other species, which have pushed P. "Msobo" into deeper layers, plays an important role here. The most southern population that we found lives near Lundo Island at the southwest point of the island. The steeply sloping bottom is largely strewn, detritus-like, with stones, interspersed by rocks. Here P. "Msobo" lives in large numbers between roughly 5 and 10 m. Juveniles formed shoals of over 100 specimens. On the southeast coast of Lundo Island, in contrast, we found no P. "Msobo" at all. In this location, facing the mainland, the bottom has a shallow slope and consists chiefly of sand and some rocks; only in shallow water is the substrate stony or rocky.

The males are strictly territorial and defend their domain vigorously. The center of the territory is a stone cave, a shelter or simply the front of a rock. Females and juveniles are soli-

*Pseudotropheus* "Msobo" (Magunga)

*Pseudotropheus* "Msobo", female (Magunga)

223

tary or live in small and rarely (see above) in large groups. *P.* "Msobo" lives primarily on Aufwuchs, which, as with *P. zebra*, is scraped off the substrate. Like all Mbunas, *P.* "Msobo" does not reject plankton. At Tumbi Rock, for example, the current carried plankton. Here even the territorial males hovered above the rocks and snapped at plankton.

## Similar species

A similar species was discovered by RIBBINK et al. (1983: 198) at the island of Likoma (Membe Point and Maingano) in deeper water between 10 and 35 m. This species was named *P.* "Membe Deep". The females of this species are also yellowish, while the males are light-blue and exhibit a black lower body half (like the population at Tumbi Reef, but without any vertical bars or blotches on the flanks). Probably these populations and the ones from Tanzania have a common origin and depending on location have evolved highly different colorations (formation of geographical races).

## Comments

Regarding the geographical variation of the male coloration, it should be noted as a trend that the northern populations (Magunga to Manda) exhibit rather irregular horizontal black pigment elements, while the middle populations (Ndumbi Reef to Lundu), which in the direction of Manda were probably restricted by the estuary of the Ruhuru, are almost entirely black with only few light-blue body blotches. The southern populations (Njambe to Lundo Island), in contrast, are light-blue and sport a more or less distinct barring pattern as well as black coloration in the lower head and body area.

In the following the color characteristics of the different populations are summarized. Keep in mind that a certain fluctuation exists even within one population in both the males and the females. Note that in general, younger females exhibit the stronger colors. Thus, at Lundo Island, we were able to observe grey-yellow (older) as well as nearly orange-yellow (younger) females. Aquarium observations have shown that older females develop approximately the coloring of males. One special aspect in this species is that brooding females acquire in an astonishing manner the respective male color-pattern for the period of hatching eggs or larvae and even adopt in most cases territorial behavior. After the final release of their brood the females gradually revert to their normal coloration.

In the accompanying photographs, we have always selected those specimens which according to our underwater observations are typical for a given population.

Magunga to Manda: males are black with light-blue elements that run primarily and irregularly through the upper body half. The proportion of the lighter elements fluctuates individually. The dorsal sports a distinct black band. Subdominant males are colored an almost uniform blue; females are yellow to orange. At Magunga, even older females are orange-colored.

Ndumbi Reef to Lundu: males almost completely black with two narrow light interorbital bars between the eyes. A few light-blue elements run in a longitudinal direction on the forehead and below the base of the dorsal. The posterior edges of the dorsal, caudal, and anal fin are conspicuously yellow. Females are colored primarily yellow, rarely grey-yellow.

Njambe to Lundo Island: males with light-blue basic coloration and narrow black barring. Lower head area as well as chest and belly are black. At Tumbi Reef, the barring in males is only hinted at (we did not, however, observe many specimens). At Puulu Island, the males sport a black band in the dorsal. At Mbahwa

*Pseudotropheus* "Msobo", subadult male
(Magunga)

*Pseudotropheus* "Msobo" (Cove Mountain)

*Pseudotropheus* "Msobo", subdominant male
(Cove Mountain)

*Pseudotropheus* "Msobo" (Cove Mountain)

*Pseudotropheus* "Msobo" (Manda)

*Pseudotropheus* "Msobo", female (Cove
Mountain)

225

Island and Lundo Island, this band is only suggested or the dorsal is purely light-blue or whitish. The females of all populations vary from grey-yellow to yellow.

P. "Msobo" has meanwhile become a popular aquarium fish. Various populations are offered commercially. One must always bear in mind that the females should always come from the same locality as the males so as to maintain the natural variation of different populations in the aquarium. P. "Msobo" has already been bred in captivity many times. The male juveniles slowly start changing into full breeding coloration at a size of ca 3 to 4 cm (1.5 to 2 months old).

*Pseudotropheus* "Msobo" (Pombo Reef)

*Pseudotropheus* "Msobo", female (Pombo Reef)

*Pseudotropheus* "Msobo" (Lundu)

*Pseudotropheus* "Msobo" (Ndumbi Reef)

*Pseudotropheus* "Msobo", female (Lundu)

226

*Pseudotropheus* "Msobo", female (Njambe)

*Pseudotropheus* "Msobo" (Njambe)

*Pseudotropheus* "Msobo", mouthbrooding female (Tumbi Rocks)

*Pseudotropheus* "Msobo" (Tumbi Reef)

*Pseudotropheus* "Msobo" (Puulu)

*Pseudotropheus* "Membe Deep" (Membe Point, Likoma Island)

*Pseudotropheus* "Msobo", female (Lundo Island)

*Pseudotropheus* "Msobo" (Lundo Island)

227

# *Pseudotropheus* "Orange Cap"

### Name

The name refers to the brownish to orange-colored head and neck area.

### Characteristics

Small, elongate Mbuna with slightly protruding upper jaw. Most specimens are ca 7 to 9 cm. Males have a blue-grey to blue basic coloration. The area from the upper lip via the anterior head up to the neck is brownish to orange-colored. The tips of the dorsal are reddish and white (Pombo Reef population). Melanin pattern, which consists of dark vertical bars, is only weakly developed and mood-dependent in the male. Females are grey to brownish.

### Distribution

We found this species at Pombo Reef and Undu Point. Further populations probably exist between these two locations that are ca 100 km apart.

### Habitat and feeding

The two populations live above stony, partly intermediate substrates at depths of about 3 to 8 m. Not a frequent species at either place. Males defend small territories whose center is usually a stony crevice, and thus are much more conspicuous than females. The latter are solitary and live relatively hidden between stones. The individuals observed by us fed on Aufwuchs.

### Similar species

At Ndumbi Reef we discovered a comparable species, *P.* "Red Top Ndumbi". With respect to body shape and also to some color elements (orange-red forehead, blue basic coloration without a distinct pattern) this cichlid is similar to *P.* "Orange Cap". The difference between these cichlids consists in their life styles — *P.* "Red Top Ndumbi" is not territorial. At the present level of knowledge, we must therefore assume that two different species are under consideration.

### Comments

The population of Undu Point does not show, in terms of coloration, a clearly delimited anterior head and neck area; rather the different colors sort of flow into each other. The author assumes that here we are faced with a geographic variation since in overall appearance and behavior the two populations are very similar. Another difference, apparent in the photographs, consists in the number of egg spots in the anal fins. However, comparative investigations must involve larger numbers of specimens, in order to evaluate this difference correctly.

*Pseudotropheus* "Orange Cap" (Pombo Reef)

*Pseudotropheus* "Orange Cap", female (Pombo Reef)

*Pseudotropheus* "Orange Cap" (Pombo Reef)

*Pseudotropheus* "Orange Cap" (Undu Point)

*Pseudotropheus* "Orange Cap" (Undu Point)

229

# Pseudotropheus "Plain"

### Name

The name refers to the inconspicuous coloration of the male, which is plain in comparison with other Mbunas.

### Characteristics

Small, somewhat stocky-looking Mbuna, attaining an overall length of ca 7 to 9 cm. The round head and the small blunt mouth are quite distinct. Males are olive-colored on the back and in the upper head region. The area below the eye and the lower flanks are bluish. The melanin pattern of dominant males consists of dark vertical bars. The dorsal sports a striking black band. The females are of a monochrome brown and besides the barring, occasionally show a mid-lateral band and another lateral band in the back area. Due to these lateral bands, a chessboard-like pattern forms in the upper body half.

### Distribution

Found at Nkanda and Kirondo. Probably further distributed in the region of the Livingstone Mountains. Not a frequently observed species.

### Habitat and feeding

At Nkanda as well as at Kirondo, we found *P.* "Plain" between stones and rocks in shallow water at depths of ca 3 to 6 m. Males defended small territories between stone crevices. Females appear to be solitary. *P.* "Plain" tends to live in hiding and owing to its not exactly eye-catching colors it is hard to detect. It is possible therefore that this species is much more frequent than our underwater observations led us to believe. *P.* "Plain" feeds on Aufwuchs.

*Pseudotropheus* "Plain" (Nkanda)

*Pseudotropheus* "Plain" (Kirondo)

# *Pseudotropheus* "Pombo Yellow Breast"

### Name

Definitive in the naming were the location of discovery at Pombo Reef and the yellow coloration of the breast.

### Characteristics

Small, elongate Mbuna, ca 7 to 9 cm in size. Upper jaw slightly protruding. The basic coloration of males is blue. The lower head area as well as the throat and chest are an intense yellow; the intensity of which is mood-dependent. Females are of a monochrome grey to brown color. The pattern in males is only visible in the form of faint, dark barring. In the females, the vertical bars are usually quite distinct. Furthermore, the females exhibit a mid-lateral and a second, weaker band in the back area.

### Distribution

Only found at Pombo Reef, where this species appears to be relatively frequent.

### Habitat and feeding

The biotope of *P.* "Pombo Yellow Breast" lies over stony and intermediate substrates in shallow water of 3 to 6 m. The males defend small territories (ca 0.5 m in diameter), whose center is usually a stone crevice or cave. The females appear to be solitary and are not loyal (or very little so) to location. *P.* "Pombo Yellow Breast", like other *Pseudotropheus* species, feeds on Aufwuchs.

### Similar species

Comparable species, with respect to body and mouth structure, are *P.* "Orange Cap" and *P.* "Red Top Ndumbi". These species, however, have different colorations. Whether these species are more closely related must be the subject of future investigation.

*Pseudotropheus* "Pombo Yellow Breast", female (Pombo Reef)

*Pseudotropheus* "Pombo Yellow Breast" (Pombo Reef)

# *Pseudotropheus* "Red Top Ndumbi"

## Name

The name refers to the orange-red dorsal and to the location of discovery — Ndumbi Reef.

## Characteristics

Small, elongate Mbuna with bluntly shaped head. Overall length ca 7 to 8 cm. Lower jaw of equal length or somewhat shorter than upper jaw. Males have blue basic coloration and orange-red dorsal and pelvic fins. In the head area from the upper jaw to the base of the dorsal, one can find very distinct orange-red spots that are strongly variable to individual. Unfortunately, we were unable to observe females.

## Distribution

*P.* "Red Top Ndumbi" was found by us only at Ndumbi Reef.

## Habitat and feeding

The village of Ndumbi lies in a sandy bay. The reef of the same name consists chiefly of large stones and rocks on a sandy bottom. Here, *P.* "Red Top Ndumbi" lives strictly rock-associated. We observed some males at depths of ca 5 to 8 m. This species does not appear to be territorial. The males swam more or less aimlessly over the bottom, grazing here and there on the algal mats. In doing so, they traversed relatively large distances (estimated: 10 to 15 m). Some males repeatedly visited the same rocks, giving rise to the impression that *P.* "Red Top Ndumbi", while not territory-forming, does prefer certain areas. In analogy to related species, this species also most probably feeds mainly on Aufwuchs.

## Similar species

Similar with respect to body shape and coloration (blue basic coloration, reddish pigmentations in head area) is *P.* "Orange Cap". This species, among other places, lives at Pombo Reef, the closest collection of rocks south of Ndumbi Reef. Regardless of the fact that these shared properties might be interpreted as an indication of a closer relationship, a crucial difference in behavior must be pointed out. In contrast to *P.* "Orange Cap", *P.* "Red Top Ndumbi" is not territorial and thus at least in the male sex practices a very different life style. The author therefore assumes that the two species are not closely related.

## Comments

At first glance, one might think that *P.* "Red Top Ndumbi" should be classified as a *Labidochromis* sp., but *P.* "Red Top Ndumbi" does not feed in the typical, plucking fashion as do the representatives of *Labidochromis* (cf. the genus text for *Labidochromis*).

*Pseudotropheus* „Red Top Ndumbi" (Ndumbi Reef)

*Pseudotropheus* "Red Top Ndumbi" (Ndumbi Reef)

Shallow bay at Ndumbi

# *Pseudotropheus tursiops*  BURGESS & AXELROD 1975

## Characteristics

Medium-sized, moderately elongate Mbuna. Total length ca 10 to 12 cm. Characteristic feature is the rounded forehead profile with the slightly protruding snout, giving this species a dolphin-like head shape (*Tursiops* is a dolphin genus). This protruding snout is particularly distinct in older specimens. Dominant males are sometimes completely light-blue, with deposits of blackish pigment in the dorsal, anal, pelvic, and caudal fins. The melanin pattern, easiest to recognize in females, consists of two lateral bands and faintly formed vertical bars. The first lateral band is clearly visible and runs through the middle of the body. The second lateral band is centered between the first one and the base of the dorsal. Both lateral bands are frequently dissolved into rows of dots. The females are grey to beige, sometimes brownish.

## Distribution

*P. tursiops* was first detected at the island of Chisumulu (BURGESS & AXELROD 1975). STAECK (1977: 180) found this cichlid in the "northeastern parts of the lake" belonging to Tanzania. Our observations refer to the populations that we encountered at Kirondo, Lupingu, and along the rocky coast north of Manda. It is highly probable that *P. tursiops* is widespread in the northern part of Lake Malawi and that it inhabits both the west and east coast (cf. Similar species).

## Habitat and feeding

*P. tursiops* prefers stony to rocky substrates in shallow water to depths of ca 5 m. The males are strictly territorial and defend their domain also against heterospecifics. *P. tursiops* is a typical Aufwuchs eater. Ribbink and colleagues, who studied the life style of this species on the island of Chisumulu, come to the conclusion that *P. tursiops* creates so-called "algal gardens" by energetically keeping all potential intruders out of his territory. In this way, only the tenants of the territory are allowed to graze on the algal mat, and compared with the neighboring surfaces one can observe a more luxurious growth of algae in their territory. At Chisumulu, 70% of the male territories could be recognized as algal gardens. These authors have also reported that the females are sometimes territorial too (RIBBINK et al. 1983: 193).

## Similar species

A closely related species is *P.* "Tursiops Mbenji" from the Mbenji Islands along the middle western coast of the lake (RIBBINK et al. 1983: 192). This cichlid differs from *P. tursiops* by the numerous black vertical bars and strong black pigmentation. The females of this species are more brownish than grey.

KONINGS (1992: 434) reported on *P.* "Tursiops Chitande", which was seen along the northwest coast in the region between Chitendi Island (English: Chitande) at Chilumba and Matambukira. Very likely these populations are conspecific with *P. tursiops*.

## Comments

*P. tursiops* is ordered within the *P.*-"Aggressive" species-group. Members of this group defend very aggressively their territories. In some species of this group even females defend territories (RIBBINK et al. 1983: 190).

*Pseudotropheus tursiops,* mouthbrooding female (Lupingu)

*Pseudotropheus tursiops* (Manda)

*Pseudotropheus tursiops* (Chirwa Island, Chilumba)

*Pseudotropheus* "Tursiops Mbenji" (Mbenji Island, aquarium photo)

235

# *Pseudotropheus* "Variable Tanzania"

### Name

This species is variable with respect to its melanin pattern. The addition "Tanzania" is necessary since certain cichlids from the northwest coast are also called "Variable" (see Similar species). More recently, this species has been offered in aquaristic circles under the name of "Labidochromis Blue Puulu".

### Characteristics

Small, somewhat stocky-looking Mbuna, which reaches an overall length of 7 to 9 cm. The basic coloration in the male is light-blue. Depending on the population as well as on the individual, the males sport black bars that become fainter in the posterior half of the body. The dorsal is whitish or light-blue with dark pigmentations that differ in intensity. The anal fin usually carries a black band. The females are a monochrome brownish color, sometimes with a bluish sheen on the flanks and in the dorsal. Juveniles are an overall yellow-brown without any pattern.

### Distribution

This species appears to be widely distributed along the Tanzanian coast. We found *P.* "Variable Tanzania" at Tumbi Rock, north of Puulu, Lundo Island, and Luhuchi Rocks (Mbamba Bay).

### Habitat and feeding

*P.* "Variable Tanzania" lives in shallow water (ca 3 to 10 m) over stony substrates. Apparently this species prefers small to medium-sized stones. The males are territorial and even chase heterospecific fish from their territories, provid-ed they can handle the intruder (owing to their small size). Center of the territory, as a rule, is a stone crevice or cave. The inconspicuous females were found by us between stones; they are solitary. *P.* "Variable Tanzania" primarily feeds on Aufwuchs.

### Similar species

For quite a number of populations, aquaristic literature uses the term *P.* "Variable" (KONINGS 1992: 434–436). These populations vary considerably with respect to coloration and sometimes the shape of the head. It remains to be clarified in future investigations whether we are concerned with races of one species or with independent species. *P.* "Variable Tanzania" shows similarities to some blue-colored populations from the northwest coast (cf. SPREINAT 1993a; *P.* cf. "Polit"). The name "Variable Tanzania" does not mean that the Tanzania populations are to be considered as conspecific with the cichlid populations mentioned before.

### Comments

The most prominent barring was found on males that we saw north of Puulu. At Lundo Island there existed males with faint barring as well as purely blue specimens, with the latter forming a majority. At Luhuchi Rocks (Mbamba Bay) we found only light-blue males without any melanin pattern.

*Pseudotropheus* "Variable Tanzania" (Lundo Island)

*Pseudotropheus* "Variable Tanzania", female (Lundo Island)

*Pseudotropheus* "Variable Tanzania" (Tumbi Reef)

*Pseudotropheus* "Variable Tanzania" (Puulu)

*Pseudotropheus* "Variable Tanzania", dominant and subdominant male (Puulu)

# *Pseudotropheus* "Yellow Tail"

### Name

The name refers to the fact that in some males the caudal fin and peduncle have an intensive yellow coloration.

### Characteristics

Medium-sized, moderately high-backed Mbuna which resembles *P. zebra* with regard to body form and shape of mouth. Overall length usually ca 10 to 12 cm. Basic coloration of males light-blue with brownish-yellow pigmentations that vary strongly with the individual. The melanin pattern consists of broad, dark-brown to black bars that partially run into the dorsal. In most cases, there is a black band in the dorsal and anal fins. The edge of the dorsal is white or yellowish. The caudal fin and caudal peduncle are yellowish. Dominant males are variable with regard to the formation of brownish-yellowish and blue colors. Females are mostly a uniform beige to light-brown, sometimes with blackish pigmentations in the pelvic and anal fins. Vertical barring is visible to a lesser degree in females and is mood-dependent.

### Distribution

Distributed at Magunga, Cove Mountain, and along the rocky coast north of Manda. Because the structure of the rocky coast remains much the same in a northern direction, it can be assumed that this species is also distributed further north.

### Habitat and feeding

Rocky and stony regions from a depth of ca 10 to 20 m form the biotope of this cichlid. The males are loyal to site and territory-holding while the females are solitary or occur in small groups of two to four individuals. At the locations mentioned above, this species is quite conspicuous. The territorial males in particular are quickly recognized by their yellow caudal fins. According to our observations, *P.* "Yellow Tail" feeds primarily on Aufwuchs which, similar to *P. zebra*, is scraped off the substrate.

### Similar species

Younger males are not as high-backed, yet, in their physique and coloration are reminiscent of some members of the *P. elongatus* species-group. Of the species living in Tanzania, *P.* "Elongatus Robust" is of particular note. *P.* "Elongatus Robust" lives in the same biotopes along the coast north of Manda as *P.* "Yellow Tail", so that the assumption that only two geographical variants of one species are concerned can be excluded.

### Comments

The males of the three populations are sometimes colored quite differently. These differences even pertain to males within one population and affect chiefly the vertical barring and the proportion of yellow-brown and blue coloration. We were unable to detect differences in the females or to distinguish the different "color forms" in a definitive way since we also saw transitional forms. Thus it must be assumed that *P.* "Yellow Tail" is a species with a wide range of fluctuation regarding male coloration.

*Pseudotropheus* "Yellow Tail" (Cove Mountain)

*Pseudotropheus* "Yellow Tail" (Manda)

*Pseudotropheus* "Yellow Tail", female (Cove Mountain)

*Pseudotropheus* "Yellow Tail" (Manda)

*Pseudotropheus* "Yellow Tail" (Magunga)

239

# The *Pseudotropheus elongatus* species-group

*Pseudotropheus elongatus* was described in 1956 by FRYER. This cichlid differed from the then known Mbunas by its unusually slender body so that the species name (elongatus = stretched out) seemed very apt (FRYER 1956). Today a number of elongate species are summarized in the *P. elongatus* species-group. RIBBINK et al. (1983: 184) listed 23 species that live along the coast of Malawi under tentative working names. Only three of these species have meanwhile been described scientifically (*P. ater*, *P. cyaneus*, *P. flavus*; STAUFFER 1988). The taxonomy of this species-group is not simple. In several cases it is not clear whether populations living along different coasts or populations resembling each other should be classified as geographical races or as autonomous species. In Tanzania we found eight species.

The representatives of this species-group are medium-sized Mbunas with a strictly stone-

or rock-associated life style. All species feed primarily on Aufwuchs. The males are mostly territorial.

It should be mentioned that *P. elongatus* was described on the basis of three specimens, which Fryer had collected along the Tanzanian coast of the lake (FRYER 1956a: 85). Although in the past in the aquaristic trade, elongated cichlids were customarily considered as *P. elongatus*, it is highly doubtful that the "true" *P. elongatus* was involved. At Mbamba Bay, we found two representatives of the *P. elongatus* species-group (*P.* "Elongatus Mbamba" and *P.* "Elongatus Ngkuyo"), which might match the first description of *P. elongatus*. Since the author has not been able to investigate the type specimens deposited by FRYER, both species are discussed here using tentative working names. (This problem is currently being investigated; SEEGERS, in preparation.)

*Pseudotropheus* "Elongatus Deep Water" (south of Mbamba Bay)

# *Pseudotropheus* "Elongatus Deep Water"

**Name**

The name refers to the preferred habitat in deep water.

**Characteristics**

Comparatively high-backed and large species. Most specimens reach overall lengths of 10 to 12 cm. The males carry dark-brown to black bars on a light-blue basic coloration. The head area is very darkly pigmented. The dorsal is black or has a broad black band. The edge of the dorsal is whitish to yellow. The posterior part of the dorsal in some specimens is also yellowish, while the anal fin is blackish. The females are uniformly light brown and exhibit a faint barring pattern. The anal fin is yellowish.

**Distribution**

We only found one population of this species, which lives along the southern rocky coast of Mbamba Bay (about the latitude of the island of Ngkuyo). Probably further distributed.

**Habitat and feeding**

The rocky coast south of Mbamba Bay consists primarily of large rocks which continue under water to a depth of about 40 m. We observed *P.* "Elongatus Deep Water" at a depth of 38 m, where this species lives between the rocks above a sandy bottom. The water appeared comparatively murky due to sediment particles. Males are loyal to site. Females and juveniles are solitary or live in loose groups. It is remarkable that we did not encounter this species in shallow water.

**Similar species**

With reference to species occurring in Tanzania, other high-backed species like *P.* "Elongatus Robust" and *P.* "Elongatus Sand" could be classified as related cichlids.

*Pseudotropheus* "Elongatus Deep Water", female (south of Mbamba Bay)

# *Pseudotropheus* "Elongatus Luhuchi"

## Name

The name refers to the discovery site: Luhuchi Rocks at Mbamba Bay.

## Characteristics

Moderately elongated member of the *P. elongatus* species-group. Total length ca 8 to 10 cm. Compared with other cichlids in this species-group the broad mouth draws attention. The basic coloration of the males is light-blue. Dominant males show a contrasting black pattern of vertical bars. The lower head and body area appear to stand out in black. The dorsal, anal, and pelvic fins are also black. The dorsal and pelvic fins show a white margin and a white trailing edge. Mature females are beige to white-grey with yellowish anal and pelvic fins. The pattern of vertical bars is only faintly visible. Young females are a uniform yellow. It is possible that all juveniles are at first yellow and then change color depending on sex.

## Distribution

We found two populations of this species along the southern border of Mbamba Bay at Luhuchi Rocks and Maunyuni Rocks.

## Habitat and feeding

Luhuchi Rocks and Maunyuni Rocks are reefs which consist primarily of large rocks and from the surface reach depths of ca 10 m. At this depth, the substrate takes the form of sandy, almost planar surfaces. *P.* "Elongatus Luhuchi" is distributed through the entire depth profile. The males live above or between the rocks and are strictly territorial. Females and subadults were found in loose groups just above the bottom. *P.*

"Elongatus Luhuchi" feeds primarily on Aufwuchs. At the time of our observations many specimens were also feeding on plankton.

## Similar species

Owing to its barred pattern and overall appearance, *P.* "Elongatus Luhuchi" resembles *P.* "Elongatus Ornatus" from the island of Likoma (RIBBINK et al. 1983: 188–189), but the latter species is more elongate. Furthermore, the females of *P.* "Elongatus Ornatus" are already beige-colored as juveniles and sport a broad black band in the dorsal.

## Comments

Due to its life style (group formation of females just above the bottom), this cichlid resembles members of the genus *Cynotilapia*. An investigation of the dentition showed that this species has bicuspid teeth and hence is indubitably to be classified as a member of the genus *Pseudotropheus*.

*Pseudotropheus* "Elongatus Luhuchi" (Luhuchi Rocks, Mbamba Bay)

*Pseudotropheus* "Elongatus Luhuchi", female (Luhuchi Rocks, Mbamba Bay)

*Pseudotropheus* "Elongatus Luhuchi" (Luhuchi Rocks, Mbamba Bay)

*Pseudotropheus* "Elongatus Luhuchi", subadult female (Luhuchi Rocks, Mbamba Bay)

*Pseudotropheus* "Elongatus Luhuchi" (Luhuchi Rocks, Mbamba Bay)

243

# Pseudotropheus "Elongatus Mbamba"

## Name

This cichlid is one of the most frequent members of the *P. elongatus* species-group in Mbamba Bay.

## Characteristics

Elongate, relatively small species which draws attention due to its blue-black coloration. The overall length is ca 8 to 9 cm. The males are blue to dark-blue with dark to black vertical bars. The formation of bars varies individually. In some males, the head and anterior part of the body appear to be black and the bars are only faintly visible in the anterior region. The posterior of the body is a uniform blue in these specimens. The females are mostly an overall dark-grey to brownish and show the suggestion of a barred pattern.

## Distribution

This species appears to be widely distributed along the Tanzanian coast. We found *P.* "Elongatus Mbamba" at Tumbi Rocks, Puulu Island, and at Mbamba Bay (Mara Rocks, Ngkuyo Island, and southern rocky coast).

## Habitat and feeding

At Ngkuyo Island, *P.* "Elongatus Mbamba" lives above large rocks to depths of ca 20 m. The males are loyal to site, but show only weakly developed territorial behavior. Females and subdominant males live in loose groups of about 20 individuals on the surfaces of rocks. Along other coastal regions we also found this species over medium and large stones. *P.* "Elongatus Mbamba" is a typical Aufwuchs feeder.

In the area of Mbamba Bay this species, together with *P.* "Elongatus Ngkuyo", counts among the most frequent members of this species-group.

## Similar species

Elongate species with blue-black coloration are also known from Malawi. Very similar is *P.* Elongatus Aggressive" from the south of the lake (Nkudzi to Mumbo Island; RIBBINK et al. 1983: 184).

## Comments

As already mentioned in the general comments on this species-group, the "genuine" *P. elongatus* hails from Mbamba Bay (FRYER 1956: 85). According to FRYER's color description, *P.* "Elongatus Mbamba" could be conspecific with *P. elongatus*. A second species that is also encountered frequently in Mbamba Bay and which due to its coloration must also be considered is *P.* "Elongatus Ngkuyo". In order to decide whether one, and if yes, which one of the two species, is to be classified as identical with *P. elongatus*, a comparative investigation is necessary (including the type specimens deposited by FRYER).

RIBBINK et al. (1983: 189) reported on *P. elongatus* of Nkhata Bay. However, it has not been proved that this population is conspecific with the specimens described by FRYER, since RIBBINK and coworkers did not carry out investigations in Tanzania. The same holds for the observations of KONINGS (1992: 373). Only when it becomes clear which cichlid of Mbamba Bay had been actually described as *P. elongatus*, can it be ascertained whether this species also occurs at Nkhata Bay.

*Pseudotropheus* "Elongatus Mbamba" (Ngkuyo Island, Mbamba Bay)

*Pseudotropheus* "Elongatus Mbamba" (Ngkuyo Island, Mbamba Bay)

*Pseudotropheus* "Elongatus Mbamba" (south of Mbamba Bay)

*Pseudotropheus* "Elongatus Mbamba" (Mara Rocks, Mbamba Bay)

*Pseudotropheus* "Elongatus Mbamba" (Mara Rocks, Mbamba Bay)

# Pseudotropheus "Elongatus Ngkuyo"

## Name

The name refers to the location of discovery: Ngkuyo Island at Mbamba Bay, where this species is frequently encountered.

## Characteristics

Medium-sized, elongate species with yellowish caudal fin. Most specimens are ca 9 to 10 cm in total length. Dominant males show a dark-brown to dark-blue pattern consisting of vertical bars on light-blue basic coloration. Head and anterior body are usually more strongly marked with dark pigmentation than the posterior regions. Conspicuous are the yellow caudal fin and the yellow posterior of the dorsal. The females are brownish to grey-blue and also carry yellow caudal fins, while the barring pattern is visible to a weaker degree.

## Distribution

We were able to find *P.* "Elongatus Ngkuyo" in the region of Mbamba Bay (northern rocky coasts, Luhuchi Rocks, Ngkuyo Island) and at Hai Reef.

## Habitat and feeding

This species can be encountered above substrates with medium-sized stones as well as in purely rocky regions. The latter seem to be preferred. *P.* "Elongatus Ngkuyo" lives in shallow water as well as at depths of 20 m. The males are loyal to site, but defend their territory comparatively weakly. Occa-sionally, we observed males and females together in loose association on the surfaces of large rocks, occupied with feeding on Aufwuchs.

## Similar species

Along the northwest coast in the region of Chilumba (Mpanga Rocks, also Chirwa Island; author's observation) lives *P.* "Elongatus Mpanga" (RIBBINK et al. 1983: 190). This species also has a yellow caudal fin and is very similar in other respects; therefore these two populations might closely related.

(Cf. the comments on *P.* "Elongatus Mbamba".)

## Comments

At Hai Reef, we found no specimens with intensely yellow caudal fins instead they were grey-beige.

Ngkuyo Island

*Pseudotropheus* "Elongatus Ngkuyo" (Ngkuyo Island, Mbamba Bay)

*Pseudotropheus* "Elongatus Ngkuyo" (Ngkuyo Island, Mbamba Bay)

*Pseudotropheus* "Elongatus Ngkuyo", female (Ngkuyo Island, Mbamba Bay)

*Pseudotropheus* "Elongatus Ngkuyo" (Ngkuyo Island, Mbamba Bay)

*Pseudotropheus* "Elongatus Ngkuyo" (Ngkuyo Island, Mbamba Bay)

247

# *Pseudotropheus* "Elongatus Robust"

## Name

The strong physique — atypical for members of the *P. elongatus* species-group — and the overall robust appearance of this species are reflected in its name.

## Characteristics

Comparatively large and high-backed cichlid that reaches an overall length of 11 to 13 cm. The basic coloration of dominant males is light-blue to whitish. The pattern consists of broad dark-blue to black vertical bars. The dorsal is either black or sports a black band. The margin of the dorsal is whitish. The females are rather brownish and also exhibit broad vertical bars. *P.* "Elongatus Robust" does not show a distinct sexual dichromatism.

## Distribution

*P.* "Elongatus Robust" is probably widespread along the Tanzanian coast. We found this cichlid at Cove Mountain, along the rocky coast north of Manda, at Mara Rocks (Mbamba Bay), and at Hai Reef.

## Habitat and feeding

Rocky, stony, and intermediate substrates are inhabited by this species. We were able to find *P.* "Elongatus Robust" distributed between shallow water (3 m deep) and depths of over 20 m. The males are loyal to site and defend their territory. The females are solitary; we found them between or above stones and rocks. *P.* "Elongatus Robust" feeds primarily on Aufwuchs.

## Similar species

Regarding the relative body depth, we must mention *P.* "Elongatus Deep Water" from Tanzania. A very similar species is also *P.* "Elongatus Sand" (see below).

From Malawi, several other species are known which might possibly form a closer group including *P.* "Elongatus Robust". The different populations from the islands of Likoma and Chisumulu (*P.* "Elongatus Mbako", *P.* "Elongatus Chisumulu", and *P.* Elongatus Gold Bar"; RIBBINK et al. 1983: 219) should also be mentioned. Another similar population was caught at "Makanjila Island" (east coast of Malawi) and described as *P. modestus* (JOHNSON 1974). Future investigations might show that many of the high-backed species could be summarized as members of a *P. modestus* species-complex.

Hai Reef is located near to the border of Mozambique.

*Pseudotropheus* "Elongatus Robust" (Manda)

*Pseudotropheus* "Elongatus Robust", female
(Cove Mountain)

*Pseudotropheus* "Elongatus Robust" (Manda)

*Pseudotropheus* "Elongatus Robust", female
(Mara Rocks, Mbamba Bay)

*Pseudotropheus* "Elongatus Robust" (Mara Rocks,
Mbamba Bay)

249

# *Pseudotropheus* "Elongatus Sand"

## Name

The life style over a sandy substrate — atypical for Mbunas — is reflected in the name.

## Characteristics

Comparatively large and high-backed member of the *P. elongatus* species-group which attains an overall length of ca 11 to 13 cm. Dominant males exhibit a melanin pattern of broad black vertical stripes on light-blue basic coloration. The dorsal is black with a white margin. The females are colored analogously, but exhibit more brownish hues.

## Distribution

We found this species at Nkanda and at the pontoon in Mbamba Bay; probably widely distributed in suitable biotopes.

## Habitat and feeding

We observed *P.* "Elongatus Sand" over sandy substrates near rocks or adjacent to the pontoon sunk at the beach of Mbamba Bay. At the pontoon, the water was between 8 and 16 m deep. Evidently *P.* "Elongatus Sand" covers vast areas over sand as this species did not seek the cover of the pontoon but lived on the surrounding sandy surfaces. Although we observed several males in full breeding colors, we could not ascertain territorial behavior. Males and females alike swam alone or in small groups. Some individuals obtained food from the substrate. At Nkanda, we caught one pair of this cichlid in a fish trap which had lain on the bottom at a depth of 56 m (measured by a depth indicator attached to the trap).

## Similar species

It is obvious that *P.* "Elongatus Sand" greatly resembles *P.* "Elongatus Robust". However, its different life style and the absence of territorial behavior in *P.* "Elongatus Sand" promote the idea that a different species is involved. Based on present knowledge, it cannot be ruled out with absolute certainty that *P.* "Elongatus Sand" is not the "sand form" of *P.* "Elongatus Robust". For the clarification of this question more detailed investigations are necessary.

The Livingstone Mountains at Nkanda.

*Pseudotropheus* "Elongatus Sand" (Pontoon, Mbamba Bay)

*Pseudotropheus* "Elongatus Sand", female (Pontoon, Mbamba Bay)

251

# *Pseudotropheus* "Elongatus Spot"

## Name

The name refers to the row of sparkling dots in the upper body half.

## Characteristics

Medium-sized, extremely elongate cichlid that reaches an overall length of ca 9 to 11 cm. Dominant males are deep-brown, nearly black. Two light-blue bars are visible between the eyes. Many Mbunas show such interorbital bars, but in this species they are particularly striking. On the anterior back, a number of vertical short light-blue lines can be recognized. These lines should be interpreted as the remainder of the light-blue basic coloration which in related species with barred patterns is still completely recognizable between the dark vertical bars. In some males the posterior area of the body, particularly the peduncle, is of a lighter color and shows traces of a barring pattern. The formation of complete vertical bars appears to be population dependent (see below). Nondominant males are light-brownish. The females are grey to light-bluish and carry the suggestion of a barred pattern. A black band runs through the dorsal and anal fins. The upper and lower area of the caudal fin also show black stripes.

## Distribution

*P.* "Elongatus Spot" occupies a large distribution area. We found this species at Puulu Island, Hongi Island, Lundo Island, along the rocky coast north of Mbamba Bay, and at Undu Point.

## Habitat and feeding

This species prefers rocks or large stones in shallow water of ca 3 to 5 m, but will penetrate to depths of at least 15 m. *P.* "Elongatus Spot" can be found quite frequently at Hongi Island. Here, males and females live on the surfaces of rocks and feed on Aufwuchs. Dominant males are loyal to site, but do not defend their territory very vigorously against other cichlids.

## Similar species

Due to the extremely elongated body shape in combination with the "glowing dots" in the upper back area this species is easily recognized. A cichlid with similar physical properties has become known as *P.* "Elongatus Ruarwe" (northwest coast) (KONINGS 1992: 384).

## Comments

In the population on Hongi Island, we found dominant males who exhibited a nearly complete barring pattern. In these specimens the bright lines extended into the lower body half, or in other words, even in the lower half the dark markings did not run into each other, but were formed as vertical bars. Furthermore it should be pointed out that the dark basic coloration in the population of Puulu Island is blue-black and not brownish as in the other populations.

*Pseudotropheus* "Elongatus Spot" (north of Mbamba Bay)

*Pseudotropheus* "Elongatus Spot", female (Lundo Island)

*Pseudotropheus* "Elongatus Spot" (Lundo Island)

*Pseudotropheus* "Elongatus Spot" (Puulu Island)

*Pseudotropheus* "Elongatus Spot" (Undu Point)

253

# The *Pseudotropheus tropheops* species-group

In the *P. tropheops* species-group, those Mbunas are summarized that have a steeply sloping forehead and a special feeding technique in common. The Aufwuchs is bitten or torn off with a lateral, upwards-pointing motion of the head. Based on this characteristic alone one can recognize the members of this species-group in the wild.

Most species inhabit the rocky or stony zone and are specialized Aufwuchs feeders. The males are territorial.

Along the coast of Malawi, 34 populations have been found (RIBBINK et al. 1983: 168). Here, the authors used the expression species-complex to clarify that a monophyletic unit is involved (cf. the introductory text on Mbunas). This means that all species or populations go back to one lineage that they alone have in common, i.e., they are all equally closely related. In the author's opinion, at least four species can be classified as a separate lineage because they are distinguished by an elongate body (*P.* "Tropheops Red Fin", *P.* "Tropheops Sand", *P.* "Tropheops Membe", *P.* "Tropheops Mumbo"; the latter species was named by the above-mentioned authors as "Zebra Mumbo", but on the basis of its feeding technique this cichlid can be classified without a doubt as "Tropheops").

Scientifically described species are *P. tropheops* REGAN 1922; *P. microstoma* TREWAVAS 1935; *P. novemfasciatus* REGAN 1922, and *P. macropthalmus* AHL 1927. While the type specimens of the first three species were collected in Malawi (TREWAVAS 1935: 75), *P. macropthalmus* stems from the northwest coast (Lumbira, formerly Langenburg) of the lake (AHL 1927: 54). Unfortunately, all of these older first descriptions are based on morphological criteria alone. At that time, it was not known that a number of closely related species exist which can barely be distinguished morphologically but that a definite differentiation can be achieved by virtue of their coloration. Since the live coloration of the specimens caught at that time remained an unknown factor, the identity of these species could not be clarified. It would require detailed detective work to prove which populations in the lake belong to the species described at that time.

Additionally, this species-group is extremely difficult to classify taxonomically, since many species very strongly resemble each other. In some locations five different species share one biotope (sympatric species), so that it is obvious that we are concerned with "true" species. For populations living along different coastal sections, however, it is very hard to determine whether we are faced with location variants of one widely distributed species or already with autonomous species.

In this context, it must be emphasized that the results presented here do not claim to be more than preliminary.

In the following, 12 species from Tanzania that are particularly frequent or seemed striking for other reasons are described. Some of these species are already known from the coasts of Malawi.

# *Pseudotropheus* "Tropheops Big Blue Yellow"

## Name

The name refers to the coloration and to the size of this species.

## Characteristics

Medium to large-sized Mbuna, reaching an overall length of ca 12 to 14 cm. Aside from the steeply sloping forehead — typical for members of this species-group — *P.* "Tropheops Big Blue Yellow" is conspicuous due to its yellow cheek and belly area in connection with the bright blue basic coloration. The formation of yellow coloring varies individually. The pattern consists of weakly formed vertical bars. The females show a silvery-blue-grey basic coloration with hints of vertical barring.

## Distribution

We found this cichlid at Lupingu, Cove Mountain, Tumbi Rocks, and Lundo Island.

## Habitat and feeding

*P.* "Tropheops Big Blue Yellow" inhabits rocky and intermediate substrates. Preferred depths lie between 3 and 10 m. Males are territorial, females solitary. Like nearly all members of this species-group, *P.* "Tropheops Big Blue Yellow" feeds primarily on Aufwuchs.

## Similar species

Of the species living in Tanzania, in particular *P.* "Tropheops Yellow Head" and *P.* "Tropheops Rusty Hongi" should be considered. *P.* "Tropheops Big Blue Yellow" differs from the above two species by its clear and vigorous blue basic coloration. Similar species from Malawi are *P.* "Tropheops Mbenji Blue", *P.* "Tropheops Lilac Maleri", and *P.* "Tropheops Yellow Chin" (RIBBINK et al. 1983: 173, 175).

*Pseudotropheus* "Tropheops Big Blue Yellow"
(Cove Mountain)

*Pseudotropheus* "Tropheops Big Blue Yellow"
(Lundo Island)

# Pseudotropheus "Tropheops Checkered"

**Name**

The name refers to the chessboard-like melanin pattern consisting of vertical and horizontal elements.

**Characteristics**

Medium-sized, moderately high-backed Mbuna with yellow-orange chest and shoulder area. The total length is ca 10 to 12 cm. The pattern consists of a mid-lateral band and a second, usually weaker band which runs centered through the upper body half. As a rule, both bands are interrupted or dissolved into rows of dots. Dark vertical bars are best recognizable in dominant males. Females show only hints of vertical barring. Remarkable is that in dominant males even the second band is fully visible so that a chessboard-like pattern appears in the shoulder region. The basic coloration of males is blue-greenish. Chest, shoulder, and anterior back are covered with yellow to orange pigmentation. The posterior operculum is also yellow-orange. Similarly colored are the pelvic fins which additionally sport a black band and a white trailing edge. Females have a grey to brownish basic coloration.

**Distribution**

We found P. "Tropheops Checkered" along the coast in the northern part of the Livingstone Mountains (Ikombe, Nkanda, Lumbira, Kirondo, and Lupingu).

**Habitat and feeding**

This species inhabits stony and intermediate substrates at depths of ca 3 to 15 m. Only rarely did we see P. "Tropheops Checkered" at greater depths. The males are strictly territorial, while females are solitary, or, depending on population density, live in small groups. P. "Tropheops Checkered" feeds on Aufwuchs, but also obtains food from the substrate or from sediment layers that have been deposited on the rocks.

**Similar species**

It is remarkable that we found this species only along the northern coast. South of the Ruhuru estuary lives P. "Tropheops Rusty Hongi". This cichlid exhibits a comparable coloration, but lacks the chessboard-like pattern in the dominant males.

*Pseudotropheus* "Tropheops Checkered", female (Kirondo)

256

*Pseudotropheus* "Tropheops Checkered" (Ikombe)

*Pseudotropheus* "Tropheops Checkered" (Kirondo)

# *Pseudotropheus* "Tropheops Chilumba"

## Name

This name has been known in aquaristic circles since the 1980s for this cichlid. Chilumba is a well-known village on the north western shore of the lake.

## Characteristics

Medium-sized Mbuna that turns high-backed with age, showing an overall length of ca 10 to 12 cm. The males are bluish to dark-blue and have black vertical bars on the flanks. The fins are blackish. The dorsal sports a white edge. Juveniles and females are a uniform orange-yellow. As a pattern sometimes vertical bars or a mid-lateral band are faintly visible. The color variability of dominant males is discussed under Comments.

## Distribution

*P.* "Tropheops Chilumba" is frequently found along the northwest coast in the region of Chilumba (Chitendi Island, Katari Island, Mpanga Rocks, Chirwa Island, Chewere; own observations). In Tanzania, we found this cichlid in Mbamba Bay at Mara Rocks. It is probably further distributed in the area of Mbamba Bay. It is remarkable that *P.* "Tropheops Chilumba" is not found — analogously to the situation on the west coast — along the northern coast of Tanzania, but instead much further south.

## Habitat and feeding

This species inhabits stony and rocky substrates. The biotope in which we observed *P.* "Tropheops Chilumba" at Mara Rocks consists of large, mostly sediment-free rocks. Along the northwest coast in the area of Chilumba, *P.*

"Tropheops Chilumba" inhabits substrates with medium to large stones and can also be found in the intermediate zone. Depending on the location, this species lives in depths of 3 to 15 m. The males are strictly territorial. As territory they usually defend a stone or rock surface. At Mara Rocks only few specimens were found, while in the area of Chilumba, *P.* "Tropheops Chilumba" counts among the most frequent representatives of this species-group. The females are mostly solitary. *P.* "Tropheops Chilumba" feeds primarily on Aufwuchs.

## Similar species

*P.* "Tropheops Black Dorsal" lives in the southeast of the lake, at West Reef and Eccles Reef (RIBBINK et al. 1983: 171); this species shows similar coloration to *P.* "Tropheops Chilumba" in both sexes. The males show a bluish basic coloration and blackish fins. The females are yellow.

## Comments

Remarkable is the color variability of the population at Chilumba. Some males exhibit a red spot on the upper end of the operculum, which clearly stands out particularly in light-colored individuals. Furthermore, some specimens show additional red pigmentations in the dorsal and pelvic fins. In rare cases nearly the entire head is red. This variation was not encountered by us in the population of Mara Rocks (Mbamba Bay). However, here we saw only relatively few specimens so that statements on color variability are somewhat restricted.

*Pseudotropheus* "Tropheops Chilumba" (Mara Rocks, Mbamba Bay)

*Pseudotropheus* "Tropheops Chilumba" (Mpanga Rocks, Chilumba)

*Pseudotropheus* "Tropheops Chilumba" (aquarium photo)

*Pseudotropheus* "Tropheops Chilumba", female (Chitendi Island, Chilumba)

*Pseudotropheus* "Tropheops Chilumba" (Chewere, Chilumba)

259

# *Pseudotropheus* "Tropheops Chitande Yellow"

## Name

The working name was suggested by RIBBINK et al. (1983: 180) who found this species, among other places, at Chitendi (English: Chitande) Island.

## Characteristics

At an overall length of ca 11 to 13 cm, this cichlid belongs to the medium-sized Mbunas. Dominant males are colored a uniform glowing yellow. In some populations the anal fin has a black band. The females are a monochrome grey and occasionally show the suggestion of a pattern of vertical bars and horizontal bands. The mid-lateral band is mostly dissolved into blotches.

## Distribution

Along the coast of Malawi, *P.* "Tropheops Chitande Yellow" is distributed at Chilumba (Chitendi Island, Chirwa Island). In Tanzania, we found *P.* "Tropheops Chitande Yellow" at Ikombe, Kirondo, Pombo Reef, and Hongi Island. Probably widely distributed in the region between Ikombe and Hongi Island.

## Habitat and feeding

Along the coast of Tanzania, we observed *P.* "Tropheops Chitande Yellow" mostly over stony and rocky substrates, rarely in intermediate zones. However, RIBBINK et al. (1983: 180) reported that along the northwest coast this species is a typical inhabitant of the intermediate zone. The males defend territories which are usually situated between or in front of stones. Due to their vibrant coloration and their territorial behavior, the males are very conspicuous.

The females are solitary and in contrast to the males quite hard to detect. Like most members of this species-group, *P.* "Tropheops Chitande Yellow" feeds primarily on Aufwuchs.

## Similar species

Another species which in the male sex has a more or less yellow basic coloration, is *P.* "Tropheops Olive" (see below). Mostly, however, this cichlid does not exhibit a purely yellow pigmentation. The lower head and body area in particular are blackish. The pattern in this species consists of distinct vertical and horizontal elements that form a chessboard-like pattern. South of the Ruhuru estuary another similar cichlid occurs, which in the following will be called *P.* "Tropheops Yellow Head". Some populations of this species also show yellow pigmentation on the flanks so that in the case of some specimens it was not clear whether we were faced with a *P.* "Tropheops Yellow Head" exhibiting especially strong yellow pigmentation or with a *P.* "Tropheops Chitande Yellow" having only a weak yellow coloration.

*Pseudotropheus* "Tropheops Chitande Yellow" (Hongi Island)

*Pseudotropheus* "Tropheops Chitande Yellow" (Ikombe)

*Pseudotropheus* "Tropheops Chitande Yellow"
(Chirwa Island, Chilumba)

*Pseudotropheus* "Tropheops Chitande Yellow"
(Kirondo)

261

# *Pseudotropheus* "Tropheops Mbamba"

## Name

The name refers to the location of discovery, Mbamba Bay, where this species occurs frequently.

## Characteristics

Medium-sized, relatively elongate representative of the *P. tropheops* species-group. The overall length of most specimens lies around 10 to 12 cm. Dominant males are bluish and show a yellow throat and chest area. Dorsal and pelvic fins are also yellowish. The anal fin carries a black band. The females are a monochrome grey to brown and show a faintly visible pattern consisting of bars and a mid-lateral band.

## Distribution

The distribution of *P.* "Tropheops Mbamba" might be limited to the southern coast of Tanzania. We found this species at Puulu Island and especially frequently at Mbamba Bay (Luhuchi Rocks, Mara Rocks, Ngkuyo Island).

## Habitat and feeding

At Mbamba Bay, the biotope of *P.* "Tropheops Mbamba" consists primarily of rocks and large stones. At the island of Puulu, we found this species also in the intermediate zone, but always oriented towards stones. The males are territorial and vigorously defend their domain which is usually located on rock surfaces or between large stones. The females appear to be mostly solitary. *P.* "Tropheops Mbamba" feeds mainly on Aufwuchs.

## Similar species

From the other Tanzanian species of this group which exhibit a comparable coloration (*P.* "Tropheops Big Blue Yellow", *P.* "Tropheops Yellow Head", *P.* "Tropheops Rusty Hongi"), *P.* "Tropheops Mbamba" is distinguished by its relatively elongated body and small size. From Malawi, similar and likewise elongate populations are known under the names of *P.* "Tropheops Lilac Mumbo" (Mumbo Island) and *P.* "Tropheops Yellow Chin" (Likoma, Chisumulu) (Ribbink et al. 1983: 173, 175). Other similar populations live along Malawi's eastern coast (Makanjila/Fort Maguire) and also along the northwest coast at Chilumba (own observations).

## Comments

The formation of yellow color in the chest and belly area evidently varies considerably within a population. At Ngkuyo Island (Mbamba Bay), we found some males in which more than half of the flanks was colored yellow.

*Pseudotropheus* "Tropheops Mbamba", female
(Ngkuyo Island, Mbamba Bay)

*Pseudotropheus* "Tropheops Mbamba" (Ngkuyo Island, Mbamba Bay)

*Pseudotropheus* "Tropheops Mbamba", female (Mara Rocks, Mbamba Bay)

*Pseudotropheus* "Tropheops Mbamba" (Puulu Island)

*Pseudotropheus* "Tropheops Mbamba" (Mara Rocks, Mbamba Bay)

*Pseudotropheus* "Tropheops Mbamba" (Ngkuyo Island, Mbamba Bay)

263

# *Pseudotropheus* "Tropheops Mutant"

We found only one specimen of this interestingly colored cichlid, a male that attracted our attention at Cove Mountain at a depth of ca 6 m. It lived at the precise border between sandy bottom and the deeper stony or intermediate zone. It intensely defended its territory of ca 1 × 1 m against all other fish. The center of the territory was the flat surface of an elongated stone (ca 1 × 0.5 m). Although we observed this male for more than 20 minutes we could not detect any females. The richly contrasting black-yellow coloration, which under water can be seen from afar, is very unusual. We intensively searched the immediate environs but could not spot another cichlid with a comparable coloration. Thus it cannot be excluded that this male presented an unusually colored specimen of *P.* "Tropheops Chitande Yellow" which due to a color mutation had formed black pigmentation. Possibly some more specimens of this interestingly colored cichlid might be found in the future so that it can be clarified whether an independent species is involved or not.

*Pseudotropheus* "Tropheops Mutant" (Cove Mountain)

264

# Pseudotropheus "Tropheops Olive"

## Name

The name was bestowed by RIBBINK and co-workers (1983: 177) who found this cichlid along the northwest coast.

## Characteristics

Medium-sized, moderately high-backed Mbuna species. The overall length, as a rule, is 10 to 12 cm. The basic coloration of males is greenish-yellow. Depending on the coloration of specific males, the black, chessboard-like pattern shimmers through as black deposits on the flanks. In dominant males the throat and lower body area are frequently black. The females are whitish to grey and exhibit a characteristic pattern consisting of dark to black vertical bars and two partially interrupted bands so that a chessboard-like pattern results. In some females even the vertical bars are interrupted. The bars are often continued as dark blotches into the dorsal.

## Distribution

In Malawi, P. "Tropheops Olive" lives along the northwest coast in the region stretching from Chirombo (south of Nkhata Bay) to about Chilumba (RIBBINK et al. 1983: 177). In Tanzania, we found this species at Kirondo, Cove Mountain, and along the rocky coast north of Manda. P. "Tropheops Olive" is probably distributed along the northern coast of Tanzania.

## Habitat and feeding

P. "Tropheops Olive" prefers biotopes with large stones or rocks in shallow water. Most specimens were observed by us at a depth of between 3 and 5 m. The males are strictly territorial and defend their domain against every intruder. The females are solitary or live in small groups. P. "Tropheops Olive", like most members of this species-group, lives on Aufwuchs.

## Similar species

Juveniles, females, and subdominant males can easily be recognized due to the chessboard-like pattern. Dominant males which have only few black pigmentations, are occasionally almost as yellow as the males of P. "Tropheops Chitande Yellow".

*Pseudotropheus* "Tropheops Olive", female (Cove Mountain)

*Pseudotropheus* "Tropheops Olive" (Kirondo)

*Pseudotropheus* "Tropheops
Olive" (Mpanga Rocks,
Chilumba)

*Pseudotropheus* "Tropheops
Olive", female (Mpanga Rocks,
Chilumba)

266

# *Pseudotropheus* "Tropheops Red Fin"

## Name

The name refers to the reddish to yellow anal fin of the females (Ribbink et al. 1983: 179).

## Characteristics

Elongate representative of the *P. tropheops* species-group reaching a total length of ca 10 to 13 cm. Dominant males are mainly yellow. The head and lower body area in some males are brownish to bluish. Varying with the individual, dark vertical bars are formed. The anal fin has black pigmentations or a black band. The dorsal is brownish to a vibrant yellow. The females have a grey to beige basic coloration. The anal fin or at least the posterior of the anal fin

is yellow to orange. Some females and juveniles also show yellow-orange pigmentations in the lower half of the caudal fin. Furthermore, the females sport a black band in the dorsal which is remarkable insofar as the males lack it or have merely a few black pigments in the dorsal. A pattern of vertical barring is only hinted at in the females. The population of Njambe shows in both sexes a coloration that deviates from that of all others (see below).

## Distribution

In Malawi, *P.* "Tropheops Red Fin" is distributed along the northwest coast in the region stretching roughly from Mara Rocks (Usisya) to Chilumba. Along the Tanzanian coast, we found

*Pseudotropheus* "Tropheops Red Fin" (Hai Reef)

267

this species at Njambe, Puulu Island, Hongi Island, Lundo Island, Mbamba Bay (Ngkuyo Island, Mara Rocks), Undu Point, and on Hai Reef. At all of these locations, P. "Tropheops Red Fin" was encountered frequently.

**Habitat and feeding**

P. "Tropheops Red Fin" inhabits both rocky and intermediate substrates and can be found at depths ranging from shallow water to at least 35 m. The males behave territorially. Usually they defend an area at the base of a rock or between stones. Some males consider the flat surface of a rock as territory and defend it accordingly. The females are solitary or live in small groups. P. "Tropheops Red Fin" feeds on Aufwuchs but also obtains food from the substrate or from sediment layers that are deposited — depending on depth and biotope — on stones and rocks.

**Similar species**

P. "Tropheops Red Fin" is conspicuous for its body shape which is very elongated compared with the other species of the P. tropheops species-group. Other elongate species are P. "Tropheops Sand" (see below) and P. "Tropheops Mumbo" from Mumbo Island. The last species mentioned — due to its coloration — might be more closely related to P. "Tropheops Red Fin". Owing to their slender body shape, these species can be separated from the high-backed members of this group (cf. the introduction to this species-group).

**Comments**

With one exception, all populations of this species — along the northwest coast as well as the Tanzanian coast — are similarly colored in both sexes. The exception is the Njambe population, which in the male sex is very dark and the dorsal has a broad black band with a white edge.

The females of the Njambe population are light-beige, but these also sport a black band with white edge in the dorsal. It is remarkable that these females do not have a yellow-orange anal fin, instead a broad black band is formed. The upper and lower areas of the caudal fin too contain black pigmentations. The biotope of Njambe also deviates clearly from the biotopes in which we normally encountered this species. Only few single stones or rocks were found on a sandy or pebbly substrate. The females of P. "Tropheops Red Fin" in particular traveled very far from the protection of the rocks to forage for food. The males defended territories at the foot of rocks. However, the population density was clearly much smaller than at other locations.

*Pseudotropheus* "Tropheops Red Fin" (Tanzania, aquarium photo)

268

*Pseudotropheus* "Tropheops Red Fin", female (Njambe)

*Pseudotropheus* "Tropheops Red Fin" (Njambe)

*Pseudotropheus* "Tropheops Red Fin", female (Mara Rocks, Mbamba Bay)

*Pseudotropheus* "Tropheops Red Fin" (Hongi Island)

*Pseudotropheus* "Tropheops Red Fin" (Ngkuyo Island, Mbamba Bay)

*Pseudotropheus* "Tropheops Red Fin", female (Ngkuyo Island, Mbamba Bay)

269

# *Pseudotropheus* "Tropheops Rusty Hongi"

## Name

The name refers to the yellow to rust-colored chest area.

## Characteristics

Medium-large, moderately high-backed member of the *P. tropheops* species-group, which reaches an overall length of ca 11 to 13 cm. Dominant males show a blue to blackish basic coloration which is particularly intensive on the head and anterior part of the body. The posterior of the operculum as well as the chest and belly area are yellowish. Depending on mood, dark vertical bars may be visible. The females are grey-brown and exhibit a pattern of vertical bars. Frequently two interrupted bands are also recognizable.

## Distribution

We found *P.* "Tropheops Rusty Hongi" at Tumbi Rocks, Hongi Island, and Lundo Island. Possibly distributed further. Not a frequently occurring species.

## Habitat and feeding

The biotope of these cichlids lies over rocky and stony substrates. Evidently, *P.* "Tropheops Rusty Hongi" prefers shallow depths; rarely did we find this species at depths deeper than 10 m. The males are territorial. We saw only few females and those were solitary. *P.* "Tropheops Rusty Hongi" feeds primarily on Aufwuchs which is plucked from the substrate.

## Similar species

A similar species is *P.* "Tropheops Checkered". This cichlid was found by us only north of the Ruhuru estuary. It is possible that *P.* "Tropheops Rusty Hongi" is either a closely related species or a southern location variant of *P.* "Tropheops Checkered".

*Pseudotropheus* "Tropheops Rusty Hongi" (Lundo Island)

*Pseudotropheus* "Tropheops Rusty Hongi" (Hongi Island)

Hongi Island and its surrounding littoral zone consists mainly of big boulders.

271

# *Pseudotropheus* "Tropheops Sand"

## Name

The name refers to the sandy habitat preferred by these cichlids.

## Characteristics

Medium-sized, relatively elongate "Tropheops" with a flat head profile. Most specimens have a total length of about 10 to 12 cm. The basic coloration of the males is predominantly brownish-yellow with a blue sheen on the flanks. Depending on mood, dark-brown vertical bars are visible. The head is dark to dark-blue. The yellow coloration extends primarily to the chest, shoulder, and anterior back. Furthermore, the males exhibit a remarkably large egg spot in the anal fin. The females are a monochrome grey to beige color.

## Distribution

*P.* "Tropheops Sand" is no doubt widely distributed along the Tanzanian coast. We found this species at Nkanda, Lumbira, Makonde, along the rocky coast north of Manda, at Lundu, and at Hai Reef (regarding the last named location cf. Comments).

## Habitat and feeding

*P.* "Tropheops Sand" inhabits sandy substrates near large stones or rocks. We found this species particularly often in deep water of ca 30 to 40 m, but depending on the nature of the substrate it also lived in shallow water of ca 5 to 10 m. Most males do not behave territorially, but roam seemingly aimlessly over the substrate. Some males show a preference for the neighborhood of rocks. Here it must be kept in mind that fish density at large depths is only slight and that few conspecifics or other cichlids are present to instigate the males to defend territories. The females are solitary, or, more rarely, live in small groups of two to three specimens. According to our observations, *P.* "Tropheops Sand" feeds mainly on organic substances and micro-organisms, which are obtained from the substrate or sediment layer.

## Similar species

Other elongate species are *P.* "Tropheops Red Fin" and the two Malawi coast species called *P.* "Tropheops Mumbo" (Mumbo Island) and *P.* "Tropheops Membe" (Likoma Island). It is possible that these elongate species form a closer family (cf. *P.* "Tropheops Red Fin").

The coloration in combination with the biotope preference is characteristic for *P.* "Tropheops Sand" so that a comparison with other species in the *P. tropheops* group is not necessary.

## Comments

The males living on Hai Reef did not exhibit just one single large egg spot in the anal fin but several smaller ones. However, with regard to life style and coloration this southern population was largely identical with the northern populations. In how far the size of the egg spot can be considered a principal difference needs to be evaluated in a larger number of specimens.

*Pseudotropheus* "Tropheops Sand" (Lundu)

*Pseudotropheus* "Tropheops Sand", female
(Lumbira)

*Pseudotropheus* "Tropheops Sand" (Nkanda)

*Pseudotropheus* "Tropheops Sand" (Manda)

*Pseudotropheus* "Tropheops Sand" (Hai Reef)

# *Pseudotropheus* "Tropheops Weed Tanzania"

## Name

In Malawi, a member of this species-group has become known as *P.* "Tropheops Weed" (RIB-BINK et al. 1983: 179). The populations occurring in Tanzania could belong to the same species.

## Characteristics

At an overall length of ca 9 to 10 cm, this is a relatively small and only moderately high-backed species of this group. The basic coloration of dominant males is light-blue. The lower head area and chest are a contrasting dark-blue or brown. Particularly in the anterior body broad black vertical bars are formed. The shoulder and chest region is covered with yellow pigmentations which sometimes extend to the upper head area. The females are a monochrome grey-brown and show a less distinct pattern of vertical bars than the males. Sometimes two weakly formed lateral bands also exist.

## Distribution

We found this cichlid at Lundo Island, at the pontoon in Mbamba Bay, and also along the southern coast of Mbamba Bay. It is possible that *P.* "Tropheops Weed Tanzania" is widely distributed along the southern coast of Tanzania.

## Habitat and feeding

*P.* "Tropheops Weed Tanzania" prefers shallow, primarily sandy regions. At Lundo Island, this species lives in depths of ca 5 to 10 m over a sandy bottom, interspersed by only a few large stones. At Mbamba Bay, we observed *P.* "Tropheops Weed Tanzania" over a sandy bottom near the sunken pontoon. The males are strictly territorial and defend their territory against all other fish. As center of their territory, they usually select a medium-sized stone lying isolated on the sandy bottom or a corresponding formation made up of several stones. At the foot of the stone, the males dig shallow depressions and an area of about 2 m in diameter is vigorously defended. If the size of the territory seems large compared with the size of the fish, one must keep in mind that in the sandy zone fish density generally is not quite as high as in the rocky zone. Thus it is possible to defend a large area with relatively small effort. Females are either solitary or seen in small groups in adjacent areas. *P.* "Tropheops Weed Tanzania" feeds on Aufwuchs and also obtains food from the substrate.

## Similar species.

As already mentioned under Name, *P.* "Tropheops Weed" from the northwest coast is a very similar species. There is a high probability that *P.* "Tropheops Weed Tanzania" is conspecific. Of the Malawi populations which occur at Dankanya Bay, Usisya, and Chitendi Island (RIBBINK et al. 1983: 179) and also according to our own observations north of Chilumba at Chewere, it is known that plants beds (= "weeds") are also inhabited.

*Pseudotropheus* "Tropheops Weed Tanzania" (Lundo Island)

*Pseudotropheus* "Tropheops Weed Tanzania",
female (Lundo Island)

*Pseudotropheus* "Tropheops Weed Tanzania"
(Pontoon, Mbamba Bay)

*Pseudotropheus* "Tropheops Weed Tanzania"
(Lundo Island)

*Pseudotropheus* "Tropheops Weed" (Chewere,
Chilumba)

# *Pseudotropheus* "Tropheops Yellow Head"

### Name

The name refers to the yellow coloration of the head.

### Characteristics

Relatively large and high-backed species of the *P. tropheops* group. Overall length of most specimens is 12 to 14 cm. Males show a bluish to blue basic coloration with varying proportions of yellow. In all populations, the lower head area is an intensive yellow. Furthermore, chest and shoulder are usually also covered with yellow pigmentations. Varying with the individual, the yellow areas may extend to the flanks. Females exhibit a white to grey basic coloration. Their pattern consists of two horizontal rows of spots which, with respect to their location, correspond to the frequently occurring two bands. Dark vertical bars can be seen in both sexes depending on mood.

### Distribution

This species appears to have a wide distribution along the southern coast of Tanzania. We observed populations at Pombo Reef, Tumbi Rocks, Puulu Island, Hongi Island, Undu Point, and Hai Reef.

### Habitat and feeding

*P.* "Tropheops Yellow Head" inhabits stony and rocky zones in shallow water from 2 to 10 m deep. Rarely did we find this cichlid over intermediate substrates. The males are strictly territorial. Their territories are usually situated between stones. Females, as a rule, are solitary. At very high population densities one can also find females in loose troops. *P.* "Tropheops Yellow Head" feeds primarily on Aufwuchs.

### Similar species

Species with similar coloration and body shape are *P.* "Tropheops Big Blue Yellow", *P.* "Tropheops Mbamba", and, with restrictions, also *P.* "Tropheops Rusty Hongi". *P.* "Tropheops Yellow Head" is distinguished by its large areas of yellow color. From Malawi several similarly colored "Tropheops" are known (RIBBINK et al. 1983). The exact relationships between many of these very similar species and location variants are not clarified definitively.

### Comments

The color variability of dominant males is so large that sometimes it seems very doubtful that only one species can be involved. According to our observations, two "forms" are recognizable. On Pombo Reef and Hai Reef the males, in a relatively uniform manner, show a yellow coloration that is primarily limited to the head, chest, and shoulder regions, while at Tumbi Rocks and Hongi Island males were found in which the yellow pigmentation extended to the flanks. Taking into consideration the complex and hard-to-recognize relationships within this species-group, at the present time it cannot be ruled out that the two forms under discussion are not independent species.

*Pseudotropheus* "Tropheops Yellow Head" (Tumbi Rocks)

*Pseudotropheus* "Tropheops Yellow Head" (Hongi Island)

*Pseudotropheus* "Tropheops Yellow Head" (Tumbi Rocks)

*Pseudotropheus* "Tropheops Yellow Head" (Hai Reef)

*Pseudotropheus* "Tropheops Yellow Head" (Undu Point)

277

# The *Pseudotropheus zebra* species-complex

*Pseudotropheus zebra* was described as early as 1899 (Boulenger 1899). In the 1980s many more species were discovered which, with respect to body shape and particularly to head shape, are very similar to *P. zebra*. These species were therefore summarized as *P. zebra* species-complex. Ribbink and coworkers (1983: 158) listed 27 species that live in Malawi. But these authors, have classified within the *P. zebra* species-complex some species which, seen on the whole, are clearly distinguishable from *P. zebra* and its more closely related species (for example, *P. elegans*, *P. lombardoi*, *P.* "Zebra Patricki", *P.* "Livingstonii Likoma"). Tanzania also has species which can be classified within this complex in a broader sense (for example, *P.* "Msobo", *P.* "Black Dorsal Tanzania", *P.* "Yellow Tail"). However, in the following we have not included such species in the *P. zebra* species-complex, only those species that are considered as "Zebras" in the narrower sense.

In Tanzania we found a total of 11 species. Only three species (*P. zebra*, *P. callainos*, *P. fainzilberi*) have been described scientifically. The former two also occur along the coast of Malawi.

With respect to the Tanzanian species, one can carry out a further division which is very helpful for identification and makes the survey more manageable. When beginning with underwater observations at any coastal section, it is at first very difficult to classify correctly the various and sometimes very similar species and their color morphs. We began with our investigations at Ikombe in the north. Here, both *P. zebra* and *P. fainzilberi* (due to its robust lower jaw and the yellow-brownish coloration of the chest), are immediately noticeable. In addition, there are *P. callainos* and a fourth species

which, due to its slender body shape and coloration, differs from the other three. This cichlid we named *P.* "Zebra Slim". Along the coast of the Livingstone Mountains (Ikombe to Manda) these four species can be observed together in many places.

South of Manda is located the estuary of the Ruhuru which for some species poses a physical barrier to their distribution. Along the southern coast we did actually find a different population composition. *P.* "Zebra Slim", or a species which could have represented a geographical form of *P.* "Zebra Slim", was no longer seen south of Manda.

*P. zebra* and *P. callainos* continued to occur. Instead of *P. fainzilberi* we found a similar species which is probably closely related to *P. fainzilberi* and thus could also be classified as geographical subspecies. This cichlid is listed in the following text as *P.* "Zebra Gold Breast Orange Top". South of the Ruhuru two further species occur, but these have comparatively small distribution areas and can easily be ordered (*P.* "Zebra Yellow Belly" and *P.* "Zebra Mbamba Bay Kompakt").

The dominant species between Ndumbi Reef and Hai Reef are *P. zebra* and *P.* "Zebra Gold Breast Orange Top" (or the allopatric population *P.* "Zebra Gold Breast Mbamba" which is probably related to the last species), which occur together in most biotopes. The classification into subgroups is best interpreted via the distribution areas. In this way it becomes clear which populations can be ordered as "true" sympatric species and which ones, in the framework of future investigations, must possibly be classified as geographical races or location variants. The following table summarizes our results.

# Distribution areas of cichlids of the *Pseudotropheus zebra* species-complex in Tanzania

| | P. call. | P. z. | P. fain. | ZGBOT | ZGBM | ZSO | ZS | ZBG | ZMBK | ZYB | ZDT |
|---|---|---|---|---|---|---|---|---|---|---|---|
| Ikombe | + | + | + | - | - | - | - | + | - | - | - |
| Nkanda | + | + | + | - | - | - | - | + | - | - | - |
| Lumbira | - | + | + | - | - | - | - | + | - | - | - |
| Kirondo | + | + | + | - | - | - | - | + | - | - | - |
| Makonde | + | + | + | - | - | - | - | + | - | - | - |
| Lupingu | | | | | | | | | | | |
|   north | + | + | + | - | - | - | - | + | - | - | + |
|   direct | + | + | + | - | - | - | - | + | - | - | - |
| Magunga | + | + | + | - | - | - | - | + | - | - | - |
| Cove Mt. | - | + | + | - | - | - | - | + | - | - | - |
| Manda | | | | | | | | | | | |
|   north | - | + | + | - | - | - | - | + | - | - | - |
| Ndumbi Reef | - | + | - | + | - | - | - | - | - | + | - |
| Pombo Reef | + | + | - | + | - | - | - | - | - | + | - |
| Lundu | + | + | - | + | - | - | - | - | - | - | - |
| Njambe | - | + | - | - | - | - | - | - | - | - | - |
| Tumbi Rocks | + | + | - | - | - | - | - | - | - | - | - |
| Tumbi Reef | - | + | - | - | - | - | - | - | - | - | - |
| Puulu | + | + | - | - | - | - | - | - | - | - | - |
| Puulu Island | + | + | - | + | - | - | - | - | - | - | + |
| Hongi Island | - | + | - | + | - | - | - | - | - | - | - |
| Mbahwa Island | - | + | - | + | - | - | - | - | - | - | - |
| Lundo Island | - | + | - | + | - | - | - | - | - | - | - |
| Mbamba Bay | | | | | | | | | | | |
|   north | - | - | | | | | | | | | |
| Luhuchi Rocks | - | + | - | - | - | - | - | - | - | - | - |
| Mara Rocks | - | - | - | - | + | - | - | - | + | - | - |
| Ngkuyo Island | - | - | - | - | + | - | - | - | + | - | - |
|   south | - | - | | | | | | | + | | |
| Undu Point | - | + | - | - | - | + | - | - | - | - | - |
| Hai Reef | - | + | - | - | - | + | - | - | - | - | - |

+ = found; - = not found; when data are absent, we did not observe the species involved and our investigations were not intensive enough to make a + / - decision.

*P. call.* = *Pseudotropheus callainos*; *P. z.* = *P. zebra*; *P. fain.* = *P. fainzilberi*; ZGBOT = *P.* "Zebra Gold Breast Orange Top"; ZGBM = *P.* "Zebra Gold Breast Mbamba"; ZSO = *P.* "Zebra South"; ZS = *P.* "Zebra Slim"; ZBG = *P.* "Zebra Blue Gold"; ZMBK = *P.* "Zebra Mbamba Bay Kompakt"; ZYB = *P.* "Zebra Yellow Belly"; ZDT = *P.* "Zebra Dwarf Tanzania";

# *Pseudotropheus callainos*

## Characteristics

Medium-sized, moderately elongate Mbuna, which reaches an overall length of ca 10 to 12 cm. *P. callainos* is a polymorphous species in which both sexes produce blue (B morphs), white (W morphs), and more rarely, dark-grey blotched (OB morphs) specimens. The B morphs show a uniformly vibrant blue, the W morphs a correspondingly white coloration. In W males, the white basic coloration is superimposed by a blue sheen, while W females appear to be creamy-white. OB specimens in the female sex show an individually varying large number of dark-grey blotches on white background. OB males are colored analogously, but show bluish blotches and the blue sheen on the flanks that is characteristic for males. OB males are very rare. A pattern is nonexistent. In some individuals dark vertical barring is faintly visible.

## Distribution

*P. callainos* inhabits large regions along the northwest and northeast coast of the lake. Along the northwest coast, this species is distributed from Kande Island (south of Nkhata Bay) to at least Chewere (north of Chilumba) (SPREINAT 1993b). In Tanzania, we also found this cichlid from the northern tip to Puulu Island (Ikombe, Nkanda, Kirondo, Makonde, Lupingu, Magunga, Pombo Reef, Lundu, Tumbi Rock, Puulu, and Puulu Island).

## Habitat and feeding

This cichlid is encountered frequently in a rocky and stony habitat and also over intermediate substrates. Most specimens live at depths of ca 3 to 10 m. Males, while preferring certain areas between rocks or above stones, hardly defend them against other fish. Both males and females, in some places, live in extended groups that may contain 20 to 30 specimens. Evidently we are faced with a cichlid with only mildly developed intraspecific aggression. *P. callainos* feeds on Aufwuchs, but like many other Mbuna, does not reject plankton.

## Similar species

The (nearly total) absence of a pattern in both sexes distinguishes *P. callainos* from the other members in this species-complex. In the classification of W and OB morphs one must keep in mind that *P. zebra* also produces these morphs. The OB and O morphs (orange) of *P. zebra* show mostly a reddish basic coloration, but there are also specimens that have few reddish pigments and consequently appear to be white. Such individuals can only be distinguished via an exact comparison of body proportions and head shapes. Furthermore, there exist some species whose dominant males are colored a uniform light-blue and which therefore look very similar to the B morphs of *P. callainos*. Here should be mentioned the populations of *P. zebra*, which have only faintly visible barring. From Malawi other species are known which in the male sex exhibit a uniformly light-blue coloration (*P. xanstomachus* from the Maleri Islands, *P.* "Zebra Blue" from Nankoma Island and Maleri Island, *P.* "Roter Zebra" from Metangula (Mozambique), *P.* "Hellblauer Zebra" from the northwest coast, and *P.* "Hellblauer Makanjila Zebra" from Malawi's east coast in the region of Makanjila/Fort Maguire; SPREINAT 1993b). *P.* "Zebra Mbenji" from the Mbenji

*Pseudotropheus callainos* (Puulu)

*Pseudotropheus callainos*, OB female (Chitendi Island, Chilumba)

*Pseudotropheus callainos* (Kirondo)

*Pseudotropheus callainos*, B male (Nkhata Bay)

*Pseudotropheus callainos*, female (Magunga)

281

island group and *P. greshakei* from Makokola Reef, while showing light-blue body coloration, exhibit an orange to red dorsal.

**Comments**

While along the northwest coast most populations contain B as well as OB and W morphs, in Tanzania we found exclusively W morphs. Since OB females are very rare in this species, and furthermore can be easily confused with the comparably frequent white-colored OB morphs of *P. zebra*, one cannot state with certainty that the OB morph does not occur along Tanzania's coasts. In contrast, the presence of B morphs can be ruled out for most populations with sufficient certainty, since these morphs are very conspicuous under water and easy to recognize.

Along the northwest coast a population is known at Ruarwe, in which the W morph occurs to an overwhelming (or exclusive?) extent (RIBBINK et al. 1983: 166; as *P.* "Zebra Pearly").

The populations from the northwest coast have been offered commercially as "Bright Blue", "Cobalt Zebra", and "Pearl Zebra". Ribbink et al. named the northern population from Chitendi Island *P.* "Zebra Chitande".

A group of *Pseudotropheus callainos* at Pombo Reef

# *Pseudotropheus fainzilberi*

## Characteristics

At an overall length of ca 11 to 13 cm, this is a relatively large member of the *P. zebra* species-complex. Its most striking feature is the enlarged lower jaw on which part of the dentition is always visible, although in the southern populations this feature is not very marked. Only *Petrotilapia* spp. exhibit a similar mouth structure. The basic coloration of dominant males is light-blue with strongly formed vertical bars. The lower head area is dark-brown to yellowish. Yellow pigmentations are also present in the throat and chest regions. The intensity of yellow coloration decreases in populations from north to south. The dorsal is whitish and in the pos-

terior also carries yellow pigmentations. Females are a monochrome brownish color with weakly formed yellow pigmentations.

## Distribution

The type specimens of *P. fainzilberi* were caught near Makonde (STAECK 1976: 489). Staeck also reports that this species is one of the most frequent cichlids in the adjacent ca 30 km stretch of coast. We found *P. fainzilberi* at Ikombe, Nkanda, Lumbira, Kirondo, Makonde, Lupingu, Magunga, Cove Mountain, and along the rocky coast north of Manda. The distribution area covers therefore the entire shore line of the Livingstone Mountains (ca 100 km).

*Pseudotropheus fainzilberi* (Kirondo)

## Habitat and feeding

*P. fainzilberi* prefers a rocky habitat in shallow water of ca 3 to 10 m. Occasionally one finds this cichlid over intermediate substrates. The males are strictly territorial and defend territories of about 1 m in diameter over or between stones. Females are solitary or are seen in small groups (rarely). *P. fainzilberi* is a typical Auf-wuchs feeder.

## Similar species

South of Manda we found comparable populations which are similar in particular to the *P. fainzilberi* populations in the region of Manda and Cove Mountain. This cichlid, named *P.* "Zebra Gold Breast Orange Top" is distinguished from *P. fainzilberi* by its yellow-orange dorsal and flattened lower jaw (cf. Comments).

## Comments

The robust lower jaw and the yellow cheek, throat, and chest areas were emphasized as the crucial features in the first description (STAECK 1976: 489), but we only found these characteristics clearly marked in northern populations (Ikombe to Makonde). In contrast, the populations at Lupingu, Magunga, Cove Mountain, and north of Manda did not show an especially conspicuous lower jaw and no yellow cheek and chest coloration; the throat alone is yellow. The difference with respect to the lower jaw structure in northern and southern populations is remarkable since feeding technique and biotope preferences — based on our observations — are exactly the same. To determine whether the special jaw structure depends on environmental factors, one would have to breed this cichlid in the aquarium and then compare the offspring of different populations with each other.

Even in the wild, the southern populations of *P. fainzilberi* are easy to distinguish from *P. zebra* since the latter species, in the region from Kirondo to Manda, has a broad white blaze.

*Pseudotropheus fainzilberi* guarding his territory (Magunga)

*Pseudotropheus fainzilberi* (Cove Mountain)

*Pseudotropheus fainzilberi* (Nkanda)

*Pseudotropheus fainzilberi*, female (Nkanda)

*Pseudotropheus fainzilberi* (Lupingu)

*Pseudotropheus fainzilberi* (Manda)

285

# Pseudotropheus zebra

(BOULENGER 1899)

## Characteristics

Medium-sized Mbuna with robust physique and usually contrasting melanin pattern of vertical bars. The overall length — depending on population — is ca 10 to 13 cm. *P. zebra* is a polymorphous species, in which BB (blue-black), OB (orange-blotched), and O (orange) morphs occur in both sexes (STAECK 1972, 1978). The normal form is the BB morph. The "standard coloration" of BB morphs in the male consists of black vertical bars over bright-blue to white basic coloration. The head and in particular the cheek region stand out due to their blue-black color. In the posterior of the body, the bars are usually more weakly formed. The dorsal is uniformly whitish. BB females are mostly a uniform dark-bluish or brownish color with a barring pattern that is more or less visible, depending on mood. The second most frequent form is the OB morph in which according to the individual a varying number of dark blotches are distributed over the entire body, including the fins, superimposed on a light background. OB males, which are much more rare than OB females, also exhibit a blue sheen and rather bluish blotches. The rarest form of all is the O morph. O females are creamy-white to orange-red. Within one population one may see whitish and orange specimens and the associated deviations. From aquarium observations, it is known that the formation of reddish pigmentation is strongly influenced by food. Carotinoid-containing food (for example, red-colored *Daphnia*) increases the intensity of yellow or red coloration. O males are the rarest of all morphs. Dominant O males show a whitish-blue basic coloration. It is remarkable that the

O morphs are only rarely purely white or purely orange. In many specimens one can recognize deposits of dark pigment, so that the borderline to the OB morph is not always distinct (cf. introductory chapter to the Mbunas).

*P. zebra* varies in dependence on locality or forms geographical races (cf. Comments; regarding the geographical variation of the Malawi populations see RIBBINK et al. 1983: 158–159).

## Distribution

*P. zebra* has a vast distribution area. In Malawi, this species occurs along the west coast from the extreme south (Nkopola, Boadzulu Island) to ca Dankanya Bay (south of Usisya) along numerous coastal sections. However, *P. zebra* does not inhabit the island groups of Maleri and Mbenji. *P. zebra* has also been found along Malawi's east coast at Makanjila/Fort Maguire and the islands of Likoma and Chisumulu (RIBBINK et al. 1983: 158). In Tanzania, we found *P. zebra* in the region from the northern end of the lake to the border of Mozambique (Ikombe, Nkanda, Lumbira, Kirondo, Makonde, Lupingu, Magunga, Cove Mountain, north of Manda, Ndumbi Reef, Pombo Reef, Lundu, Njambe, Tumbi Rocks, Tumbi Reef, Puulu, Puulu Island, Hongi Island, Mbahwa Island, Lundo Island, Luhuchi Rocks (Mbamba Bay), Undu Point, and Hai Reef). Only at Mara Rocks and Ngkuyo Island we did not see *P. zebra*.

## Habitat and feeding

*P. zebra*, in its vast distribution area, inhabits quite different biotopes. Most frequently one finds this species over stony or rocky substrates in shallow water of ca 3 to 15 m. Intermediate

*Pseudotropheus zebra* (Kirondo)

*Pseudotropheus zebra*, OB female (Nkanda)

*Pseudotropheus zebra* (Nkanda)

*Pseudotropheus zebra*, OB female (Cove Mountain)

*Pseudotropheus zebra*, O female (Cove Mountain)

287

substrates are also inhabited. Sometimes one even finds this cichlid in Vallisneria beds. The males are territorial and defend their domains between stones or on the surface of rocks. The females are solitary or live in groups. *P. zebra* feeds primarily on Aufwuchs. Plankton is also consumed, especially by the non-territorial specimens (FRYER 1959; HOLZBERG 1978).

### Similar species

With reference to the populations along the Tanzanian coast, there are primarily *P. fainzilberi*, *P.* "Zebra Gold Breast Orange Top", *P.* "Zebra Gold Breast Mbamba", and *P.* "Zebra South". In the following, we summarize the differences between the various populations.

In the region from Nkanda to roughly Makonde, *P. zebra* can be distinguished from *P. fainzilberi* by the fact that *P. fainzilberi* has a stronger lower jaw with partly visible dentition and yellow pigmentations on the cheek and chest region. In the more southern populations of *P. fainzilberi* these features are not developed. Despite this fact both species can be distinguished easily, since *P. zebra* in the coastal region from roughly Kirondo to Manda sports a large white blaze on its forehead.

South of Manda, instead of *P. fainzilberi*, another similar species occurs, namely *P.* "Zebra Gold Breast Orange Top". This cichlid was found living communally with *P. zebra* at Ndumbi Reef, Pombo Reef, Lundu, Puulu Island, Hongi Island, Mbahwa Island, and Lundo Island. *P.* "Zebra Gold Breast Orange Top" is distinguished from *P. zebra* by its yellow-orange dorsal and the yellow pigmentation in the throat area.

South of Lundo Island, we found along with *P.* "Zebra Gold Breast Mbamba" another similar population at Mbamba Bay (Mara Rocks and Ngkuyo Island). At these two localities *P. zebra* no longer occurs. *P.* "Zebra Gold Breast Mbamba" has a white dorsal, but shows yellow pigmentations in the throat region.

At Undu Point and Hai Reef, *P.* "Zebra South" lives sympatrically with *P. zebra*. *P.* "Zebra South" has narrow black vertical bars and sports a black band or blackish pigmentations in the dorsal. Owing to this dorsal coloration one can also recognize the females of *P.* "Zebra South".

Other similar species are *P.* "Zebra Slim" and *P.* "Zebra Mbamba Bay Kompakt". *P.* "Zebra Slim" is distributed along the northeast coast between Ikombe and Manda and occurs in many biotopes together with *P. zebra*. *P.* "Zebra Slim" is more elongate. The females of this species are of lighter color and have yellow unpaired fins.

*P.* "Zebra Mbamba Bay Kompakt" inhabits the rocky coast south of Mbamba Bay and also at Ngkuyo Island and Mara Rocks. In these regions, we were not able to detect *P. zebra*. *P.* "Zebra Mbamba Bay Kompakt" is much more slender than *P. zebra*.

*Pseudotropheus zebra* (Manda)

*Pseudotropheus zebra*, O female (Manda)

*Pseudotropheus zebra*, O female (Manda)

*Pseudotropheus zebra*, female (Manda)

*Pseudotropheus zebra* (Ndumbi Reef)

## Comments

Remarkable is the geographical variation of dominant BB males, which with respect to the Tanzanian coastline can be summarized as follows (from north to south):

**Ikombe, Nkanda, Lumbira:** these populations display the "standard" coloration as it is also known from many populations in Malawi (for example, at Monkey Bay or Nkhata Bay).

**Kirondo, Makonde, Lupingu, Magunga, Cove Mountain, north of Manda:** at these localities the males sport a large white blaze running from the snout to the base of the dorsal. These specimens are somewhat smaller than those in other populations.

**Ndumbi Reef, Pombo Reef:** these populations show only a weakly developed barring pattern. Dominant males are primarily a uniform bright-blue with a hint of vertical barring.

**Lundu, Njambe:** in these populations the standard coloration again prevails.

**Tumbi Rocks, Tumbi Reef:** standard coloration with conspicuously broad black stripe in upper head area.

**Puulu, Puulu Island, Hongi Island, Mbahwa Island:** standard coloration.

**Lundo Island:** standard coloration with broad blaze on forehead.

**Luhuchi Rocks:** standard coloration.

**Undu Point, Hai Reef:** here the BB males show a weakly formed barred pattern. Most males are a uniform bright-blue like the populations at Ndumbi Reef and Pombo Reef.

*Pseudotropheus zebra* (Pombo Reef)

*Pseudotropheus zebra*, O male (Pombo Reef)

*Pseudotropheus zebra*, young male (below) and female (Pombo Reef)

*Pseudotropheus zebra* (Lundu)

*Pseudotropheus zebra* (Njambe)

*Pseudotropheus zebra* (Tumbi Rocks)

*Pseudotropheus zebra* (Puulu)

*Pseudotropheus zebra,* O female (Tumbi Rocks)

*Pseudotropheus zebra*, O female (Puulu Island)

*Pseudotropheus zebra*, OB female (Puulu Island)

*Pseudotropheus zebra*, OB female (Puulu Island)

*Pseudotropheus zebra* (Lundo Island)

*Pseudotropheus zebra*, O male (Lundo Island)

*Pseudotropheus zebra* (Hai Reef)

*Pseudotropheus zebra* (Luhuchi Rocks, Mbamba Bay)

*Pseudotropheus zebra* (Undu Point)

*Pseudotropheus zebra*, O female (Hai Reef)

*Pseudotropheus zebra*, OB female (Hai Reef)

293

# *Pseudotropheus* "Zebra Blue Gold"

## Name

The name refers to the blue and yellow to gold coloration of dominant males.

## Characteristics

Small to medium-sized, elongate Mbuna, which usually reaches an overall length of 9 to 10 cm. Males exhibit a yellow basic coloration. On the anterior part of the head and back, a bright blue coloration is visible. The dorsal is also bluish, especially in its anterior part. The blue coloration varies individually. A few light-blue vertical bars occur mostly on the upper flanks. Females are a uniform yellow with the suggestion of a barred pattern.

## Distribution

We only observed one population of this species. The locality is ca 500 m north of the church of Lupingu.

## Habitat and feeding

We found this cichlid in a small cove whose bottom in shallow water consisted of an intermediate substrate. At ca 3 m the bottom shelved steeply, ravine-like, to depths of 40 m. Here *P.* "Zebra Blue Gold" lives at the border to an intermediate substrate and at the rocky steep walls to a depth of ca 20 m. Most specimens were encountered in shallow water. The males defended territories whose center was formed by a pile of stones or by rock shelters. The females lived in loose groups above the intermediate substrate or along the steep walls. *P.* "Zebra Blue Gold" fed primarily on Aufwuchs. Some specimens hovered at some distance from the bottom and snapped at plankton.

## Similar species

The above-described locality was the only one in which we did not encounter *P.* "Zebra Slim". We found *P.* "Zebra Slim" both to the north (Makonde) and in the southern Bay of Lupingu. The ravine in which we observed *P.* "Zebra Blue Gold" borders in the south on the northern sand bay of Lupingu. It can be assumed that *P.* "Zebra Blue Gold" represents a location variant of *P.* "Zebra Slim". In favor of this argument, we cite the slender body shape and the fact that the females of *P.* "Zebra Slim" are also colored grey-yellow and exhibit yellow unpaired fins. Should this conjecture hold true, it would make *P.* "Zebra Slim" a species that is colored very variably over a relatively small coastal section. To clarify this question, one would have to examine the populations of *P.* "Zebra Blue Gold" north of this locality up to the bordering populations of *P.* "Zebra Slim" in a grid as small as possible so as to find potential "transitional forms". Our next diving place north of the ravine was Makonde. The population of *P.* "Zebra Slim" living here is blue and shows dark vertical barring.

*Pseudotropheus* "Zebra Blue Gold" (north of Lupingu)

*Pseudotropheus* "Zebra Blue Gold", female (north of Lupingu)

*Pseudotropheus* "Zebra Blue Gold" (north of Lupingu)

*Pseudotropheus* "Zebra Blue Gold" (north of Lupingu)

*Pseudotropheus* "Zebra Blue Gold", females (north of Lupingu)

295

# Pseudotropheus "Zebra Dwarf Tanzania"

### Name

The name refers to the small size of this cichlid.

### Characteristics

Small, moderately elongate, and relatively inconspicuous Mbuna. Overall length is only ca 6 to 8 cm. Males are brownish-yellow and show a bluish sheen on the flanks. The pattern consists of broad dark or black vertical bars. The anal and pelvic fins are black. The dorsal sports a clearly visible black submarginal band and a white or yellow edge. Females are light-brown and also show broad dark vertical barring. The posterior part of the anal fin is yellowish. The dorsal has a band that is not as strongly marked as in the male. According to our observations, this species does not develop color morphs.

### Distribution

We found this cichlid ca 500 m north of Lupingu (same locality as P. "Zebra Blue Gold") and at Puulu Island.

### Habitat and feeding

P. "Zebra Dwarf Tanzania" inhabits deep layers over intermediate substrates. We observed this species only below 30 m. The males defended small territories near stones. The females lived alone between stones and above the adjacent sand surfaces. P. "Zebra Blue Gold" fed on Aufwuchs and food particles that were obtained from the sandy substrate.

### Similar species

We found no comparable species in Tanzania. A cichlid that is similar under certain restrictions is known as P. "Zebra Dumpy" from the islands of Maleri and Nakanthenga in the southwest of the lake (RIBBINK et al. 1983: 196). This species also lives in deep water in the intermediate zone or over sediment-rich rocky regions.

### Comments

Of all the members of this species-complex from Tanzania, P. "Zebra¹ Dwarf Tanzania" seems to be related only remotely to P. zebra. It is possible that future research will show that this cichlid is more closely related to other Pseudotropheus spp. and thus should be classified in a different group.

Pseudotropheus "Zebra Dwarf Tanzania", female (north of Lupingu)

*Pseudotropheus* "Zebra Dwarf Tanzania" (north of Lupingu)

*Pseudotropheus* "Zebra Dwarf Tanzania" (Puulu Island)

# *Pseudotropheus* "Zebra Gold Breast Mbamba"

## Name

This cichlid does not exhibit a golden chest, but merely a yellow throat area. The tentative working name reflects the close relationship to *P.* "Zebra Gold Breast Orange Top" and its distribution in Mbamba Bay.

## Characteristics

Medium-sized Mbuna with robust physique. Most specimens have an overall length of 11 to 13 cm. The basic coloration of dominant males is bright-blue to whitish. The lower head region is dark-blue, the throat orange-yellow. The pattern consists of dark-blue to black vertical bars which become fainter in the posterior of the flanks. The dorsal is uniformly bright-blue to white, and so are the anal and caudal fins. Yellow or orange pigmentations are occasionally present in the pelvic fins. Females are colored dark to brownish, with an analogous pattern. Interestingly enough, the females sport a light yellowish dorsal (see below). We did not find color morphs.

## Distribution

The distribution of this cichlid appears to be very limited. We found *P.* "Zebra Gold Breast Mbamba" exclusively along Mara Rocks and Ngkuyo Island offshore of Mbamba Bay.

## Habitat and feeding

At the localities mentioned, the substrate consists primarily of large stones and rocks. *P.* "Zebra Gold Breast Mbamba" inhabits depths of ca 3 to 10 m. Only rarely did we encounter this species in deeper water. The males are territorial. Mostly they defend their domain between rocks or on the surface of rocks. Females are solitary or seen in loose groups. *P.* "Zebra Gold Breast Mbamba" feeds primarily on Aufwuchs.

## Similar species

The species closest to *P.* "Zebra Gold Breast Mbamba" is probably P. "Zebra Gold Breast Orange Top". This cichlid inhabits numerous coastal sections north of Mbamba Bay from Lundo Island to Ndumbi Reef. *P.* "Zebra Gold Breast Mbamba" — in contrast to *P.* "Zebra Gold Breast Orange Top" — has not an orange-yellow but a white dorsal in the male sex. Furthermore, only the throat, but not the chest, is colored yellow. In constrast, it is hard to distinguish between the females of these species as they both show yellow pigmentations in the dorsal.

Owing to this great similarity and excepting any clear morphological differences, *P.* "Zebra Gold Breast Mbamba" could well be classified as a geographical subspecies or location variant of P. "Zebra Gold Breast Orange Top". We were unable to detect *P. zebra* at Mara Rocks and Ngkuyo Island. However, we did find *P. zebra* on the southern edge of Mbamba Bay at Luhuchi Rocks. The BB males of this population exhibit the standard coloration (cf. Comments under *P. zebra*).

## Comments

This cichlid was discovered by Seegers and introduced to Germany under the term *P.* spec. aff. *zebra* "Tansania" (SEEGERS 1992).

*Pseudotropheus* "Zebra Gold Breast Mbamba"
(Ngkuyo Island, Mbamba Bay)

*Pseudotropheus* "Zebra Gold Breast Mbamba"
(Ngkuyo Island, Mbamba Bay)

*Pseudotropheus* "Zebra Gold Breast Mbamba",
female (Mara Rocks, Mbamba Bay)

*Pseudotropheus* "Zebra Gold Breast Mbamba" (Mara Rocks, Mbamba Bay)

# Pseudotropheus "Zebra Gold Breast Orange Top"

## Name

The name emphasizes the characteristic color features of this cichlid (golden chest and orange-colored dorsal).

## Characteristics

Medium-sized Mbuna with robust physique, reaching an overall length of ca 11 to 13 cm. Dominant males exhibit a bright-blue basic coloration with individually varying broad, black vertical bars. The dorsal is yellow to orange. In some populations, some specimens also have a degree of black pigmentation in the dorsal; the throat and chest areas are yellowish. The extent of yellow chest coloration varies with the individual. As a trend, we observed that the northern populations (Ndumbi Reef, Pombo Reef) showed more yellow hues than the populations from Puulu to Lundo Island. Females are brownish with a suggestion of vertical bar pattern.

At Lundo Island, we also observed — apart from the BB morphs — OB and O morphs in both sexes. The OB and O morphs have a yellow dorsal, throat and chest areas which distinguishes them from the corresponding color morphs of *P. zebra*.

## Distribution

We found *P.* "Zebra Gold Breast Orange Top" at Ndumbi Reef, Pombo Reef, Lundu, Puulu Island, Hongi Island, Mbahwa Island, and Lundo Island.

## Habitat and feeding

This cichlid inhabits rocky and stony, rarely intermediate, substrates in shallow water ranging from 3 to 15 m. The depth distribution varies with the locality. At Lundo Island (southeast shore) we found the highest population density in ca 3 to 6 m. At Mbahwa Island, in contrast, *P.* "Zebra Gold Breast Orange Top" lives most often at depths between 6 and 10 m.

Males defend territories. The center of a territory consists of stone caves or other stone configurations offering the options of retreat or refuge. Females are solitary or live in loose groups. *P.* "Zebra Gold Breast Orange Top" is a typical Aufwuchs feeder.

## Similar species

The species most closely related are indubitably *P.* "Zebra Gold Breast Mbamba" (see above) and *P. fainzilberi*. Regarding their distribution these species do not overlap. The southern populations of *P. fainzilberi* are very similar with respect to their entire appearance but do not exhibit the yellow dorsal and yellow chest area (cf. the corresponding explanations under *P. fainzilberi*). *P.* "Zebra Gold Breast Mbamba" can be distinguished on the basis of its white dorsal and might be a geographical subspecies or location variant of *P.* "Zebra Gold Breast Orange Top".

(Regarding the distinction from *P. zebra* see *P. zebra*, Similar species).

*Pseudotropheus* "Zebra Gold Breast Orange Top", O male (Lundo Island)

*Pseudotropheus* "Zebra Gold Breast Orange Top"
(Ndumbi Reef)

*Pseudotropheus* "Zebra Gold Breast Orange Top"
(Pombo Reef)

*Pseudotropheus* "Zebra Gold Breast Orange Top"
(Mbahwa Island)

*Pseudotropheus* "Zebra Gold Breast Orange Top"
(Lundo Island)

# Pseudotropheus "Zebra Mbamba Bay Kompakt"

## Name

This cichlid was discovered by FLEISCHER & ENGELS and introduced to Germany in January 1990 (SEEGERS 1990). Seegers called this species *P.* spec. "Mbamba Bay Kompakt". In the author's opinion, this is a member of the *P. zebra* species-complex so that the name should be amended accordingly.

## Characteristics

Medium-sized, elongate Mbuna. Most specimens reach an overall length of ca 10 to 11 cm. *P.* "Zebra Mbamba Bay Kompakt" resembles *P. zebra* in every respect except for its much more slender body form. Dominant males (BB morphs) show a bright-blue to white basic coloration with many, sometimes densely spaced, vertical bars. The lower half of the head is prominent due to its dark-blue hues. The dorsal is uniformly white. The females are altogether brownish with only the suggestion of a barring pattern. *P.* "Zebra Mbamba Bay Kompakt" also occurs as OB morph in both sexes. We did not see any O morphs.

## Distribution

SEEGERS reported (1990) that he was able to find this cichlid along the rocky shores on the southern border of Mbamba Bay and at Ngkuyo Island, but not along the coast north of Mbamba Bay. Our observations confirm Seegers' results. We furthermore found *P.* "Zebra Mbamba Bay Kompakt" at Mara Rocks (north of Ngkuyo Island). We did not see this cichlid at Undu Point or Hai Reef.

## Habitat and feeding

At the localities mentioned, large stones and rocks define the underwater landscape. *P.* "Zebra Mbamba Bay Kompakt" lives strictly rock-associated, sometimes even hidden. The depths at which we encountered this cichlid varied from 3 to 20 m. The males defend areas between large stones or rocks against all other fish. Females are solitary, rarely living in small groups. *P.* "Zebra Mbamba Bay Kompakt", according to our underwater observations, feeds primarily on Aufwuchs.

## Similar species

As already mentioned, this is a cichlid which, except for its elongate body, resembles *P. zebra*. *P.* "Zebra Mbamba Bay Kompakt" and *P. zebra* do not overlap in their distribution areas. During our underwater observations, we immediately gained the impression that *P.* "Zebra Mbamba Bay Kompakt" occupies the same ecological niche as *P. zebra*. At Luhuchi Rocks, where we searched for *P.* "Zebra Mbamba Bay Kompakt", we only found *P. zebra*. Along the southern rocky coast of Mbamba Bay we again registered *P.* "Zebra Mbamba Bay Kompakt" but not *P. zebra*.

In this context, it is remarkable that *P. zebra*, along the western shore of the lake, did not settle at the island groups of Mbenji and Maleri. Instead, other cichlids of this species-complex are represented there. Ngkuyo Island and Mara Rocks, while not far removed from the mainland, might be separated from it by very deep water. What this "island hypothesis" does not explain, however, is the occurrence of *P.* "Zebra Mbamba Bay Kompakt" along the southern coast of Mbamba Bay. One must also keep in mind that *P. zebra* is at home on the islands of Likoma and Chisumulu, located farther out in the lake. At the present time there is not sufficient knowledge for giving a logical explanation for the colonization of specific coastal sections by Mbuna cichlids.

*Pseudotropheus* "Zebra Mbamba Bay Kompakt" (Ngkuyo Island, Mbamba Bay)

*Pseudotropheus* "Zebra Mbamba Bay Kompakt" (south of Mbamba Bay)

*Pseudotropheus* "Zebra Mbamba Bay Kompakt", OB female (Ngkuyo Island, Mbamba Bay)

*Pseudotropheus* "Zebra Mbamba Bay Kompakt", OB male (Ngkuyo Island, Mbamba Bay)

# Pseudotropheus "Zebra Slim"

## Name

The tentative working name refers to the body shape which is slim compared to that of *P. zebra*.

## Characteristics

Small to medium-sized, relatively elongate member of the *P. zebra* species-complex. The overall length is usually 8 to 10 cm. The basic coloration of dominant males is light-blue. Depending on population, vertical bars are more or less distinct. The lower head area is usually dark-blue. The dorsal is uniformly white or light-blue. The females are grey to light-brown and sport yellow unpaired fins. We did not observe color morphs in this species.

## Distribution

*P.* "Zebra Slim" inhabits the coastal region of the Livingstone Mountains. We found this cichlid at Ikombe, Nkanda, Lumbira, Kirondo, Makonde, in the southern bay of Lupingu, Magunga, Cove Mountain, and along the rocky shores north of Manda. South of the Ruhuru estuary we could no longer see this species.

## Habitat and feeding

The preferred biotope is formed by stony to rocky substrates and also by the intermediate zone. *P.* "Zebra Slim" preferably dwells between or above small and medium-sized stones. Dominant males have territories between stones or other hiding places and are frequently encountered from shallow water to depths of 10 to 15 m. Females are mostly solitary. Depending on population density females are also seen in groups. At Magunga, we found mostly juveniles and some larger females in large extended groups in shallow water of ca 1 to 2 m.

*P.* "Zebra Slim" seems to live chiefly on Aufwuchs. In some locations we observed how this species hovered just above the substrate, snapping at plankton.

## Similar species

A geographical form or location variant of *P.* "Zebra Slim" might be *P.* "Zebra Blue Gold". This cichlid was encountered north of Lupingu (cf. data for *P.* "Zebra Blue Gold").

At all localities, *P.* "Zebra Slim" lives sympatrically with *P. zebra* and *P. fainzilberi*. When not fully colored, younger males of *P.* "Zebra Slim" and *P. zebra* are very similar to each other.

A cichlid that is especially similar to the population of Magunga with respect to body shape and coloration is *P.* "Kingsizei" from the island of Likoma (RIBBINK et al. 1983: 198; GERHARDT & SPREINAT 1989). *P.* "Kingsizei" females are also light-brown with yellow unpaired fins. Both species probably belong to the same lineage.

*Pseudotropheus* "Zebra Slim" (Kirondo)

*Pseudotropheus* "Zebra Slim" (Lumbira)

*Pseudotropheus* "Zebra Slim" (Nkanda)

*Pseudotropheus* "Zebra Slim", female (Magunga)

*Pseudotropheus* "Zebra Slim" (Magunga)

# *Pseudotropheus* "Zebra South"

## Name

The name refers to the distribution area which lies at the southern end of the Tanzanian coastline.

## Characteristics

Large and robust representative of the *P. zebra* species-complex which reaches a total length of 12 to 14 cm. Males in breeding colors show a light-blue to white basic coloration with relatively narrow vertical bars. The cheek and chest areas are of a somewhat darker blue. The dorsal is white with an individually variable, strongly formed band. This band or just black pigmentations can also be seen in the females. The latter are dark-blue to brownish with faint vertical bars. We did not see either OB or O morphs.

## Distribution

We found this cichlid at Undu Point and Hai Reef.

## Habitat and feeding

Rocky habitats rich in sediment and intermediate substrates are typical for Undu Point and Hai Reef. Most specimens were observed by us in shallow water between 3 and 8 m. The males are territorial and defend their domain against all other fish. In most cases, a cave-like shelter is the focus of their territory. The females are solitary, or more seldom, are seen in small groups. *P.* "Zebra South" feeds on Aufwuchs but also forages for food in the layers of sediment.

## Similar species

The *P. zebra* populations living at Undu Point and Hai Reef show only faint banding and in the male sex are predominantly a uniform light-blue, so that the two species can easily be separated. The females of *P.* "Zebra South" show a black band in the dorsal which does not exist in females of *P. zebra*.

In analogy to the northern coastline where *P. zebra* lives sympatrically in many biotopes with *P.* "Zebra Gold Breast Orange Top", one might speculate that *P.* "Zebra South" is a southern "offspring" of *P.* "Zebra Gold Breast Orange Top". At the present level of knowledge this question remains unanswered and must be the subject of more detailed investigations.

Undu Point is a small isolated rocky area on a long sandy beach.

*Pseudotropheus* "Zebra South" (Undu Point)

*Pseudotropheus* "Zebra South", female (Hai Reef)

307

# *Pseudotropheus* "Zebra Yellow Belly"

### Name

The conspicuous yellow belly is the characteristic feature of this cichlid.

### Characteristics

At an overall length of ca 10 to 12 cm, this relatively elongate species belongs to the medium-sized Mbunas. The basic coloration of dominant males is light-blue, nearly white. Especially on the anterior flanks one can see dark-blue to brown vertical bars spread relatively far apart. The lower head area as well as the throat, chest, and belly are light to dark yellow. In some specimens this yellow coloration extends above and into the anal fin. The dorsal is uniformly yellow. The females are beige to grey with a faint pattern of vertical bars. Black pigmentations are usually present in the anal and caudal fins. Even the females sport a slightly yellow dorsal. This species does not seem to develop OB or O morphs.

### Distribution

We found *P.* "Zebra Yellow Belly" at Ndumbi Reef and Pombo Reef where this Mbuna is among the more frequent species.

### Habitat and feeding

*P.* "Zebra Yellow Belly" was found by us over intermediate substrates. Most specimens live in shallow water of ca 3 to 8 m. The males defend territories of about 1.5 m in diameter between stones or on the surface of rocks. The females are mostly solitary and dwell between the male territories. *P.* "Zebra Yellow Belly" scrapes Aufwuchs off stones. In some cases we observed how this species also takes food from the sandy bottom between stones. This cichlid was not shy at all towards the diver but seemed rather curious.

### Similar species

*P.* "Zebra Yellow Belly" at both localities lives sympatrically with *P. zebra* and *P.* "Zebra Gold Breast Orange Top". The latter species in principle is colored similarly, but is clearly more high-backed.

Two species from Malawi, that with restrictions are comparably colored in the male sex, are *P. hajomaylandi* from Chisumulu Island (cf. RIBBINK et al. 1983: 164; as *P.* "Zebra Greberi") and *P. aurora* from Likoma Island.

*Pseudotropheus hajomaylandi* (Chisumulu)

*Pseudotropheus* "Zebra Yellow Belly" (Ndumbi Reef)

*Pseudotropheus* "Zebra Yellow Belly" (Ndumbi Reef)

*Pseudotropheus* "Zebra Yellow Belly", female (Ndumbi Reef)

*Pseudotropheus* "Zebra Yellow Belly" (Pombo Reef)

*Pseudotropheus aurora* (Likoma)

309

# References

AHL, E. (1927): Einige neue Fische aus der Familie Cichlidae aus dem Nyassa-See. Schr. berl. Ges. naturf. Fr. Berl. 1926, 51–62.

AX, P. (1987): The Phylogenetic System. Wiley & Son, Chichester, New York, 349 pp.

Bentler, A. (1993): Neuere Importe aus dem Malawisee. Das Aquarium 27 (286), 42.

BOULENGER, G.A. (1899): A revision of the African and Syrian fishes of the family Cichlidae. Part II. Proc. zool. Soc. Lond. 1899: 98–143.

BOULENGER, G.A. (1901): Diagnoses of four new fishes discovered by Mr. J.E.S. MOORE in Lakes Tanganjika and Kivu. Ann. Mag. nat. Hist. 8 (7), 1–6.

BOULENGER, G.A. (1902): Diagnoses of new cichlid fishes discovered by Mr. J. E. S. MOORE in Lake Nyasa. Ann. Mag. nat. Hist. 10 (7), 1–6.

BOULENGER, G.A. (1908): Diagnoses of new fishes discovered by Capt. E. L. RHOADES in Lake Nyasa. Ann. Mag. nat. Hist. 2 (8), 238–243.

BOULENGER, G.A. (1915): Catalogue of the freshwater fishes of Africa in the British Museum (Natural History). Br. Mus. nat. Hist. Lond. Vol. 3, 526 pp.

BURGESS, W.E. & H.R. AXELROD (1975): *Pseudotropheus tursiops*, a new species of cichlid from Lake Malawi. Tropical Fish Hobbyist 24 (Nov. 1975), 86–90.

BURGESS, W.E. & H.R. AXELROD (1976): Studies on the family Cichlidae: 4. Two new species of Mbuna (rock-dwelling cichlids) from Lake Malawi. Tropical Fish Hobbyist 24 (März 1976), 44–48.

DEMASON, L. (1993a): Ähnliche Arten an den gegenüberliegenden Küsten im nördlichen Malawisee – weitere Hinweise für eine stufenweise Artbildung? Das Cichlidenjahrbuch, Cichlid Press, St. Leon-Rot, 37–40.

DEMASON, L. (1993b): Into Africa: Exploring the Tansanian coast of Lake Malawi – Part I. Cichlid News, 2 (4), 22–23.

DEMASON, L. (1993c): What's new. Cichlid News, 2 (4), 27.

DEMASON, L. (1994a): Into Africa: Exploring the Tansanian coast of Lake Malawi – Part II. Cichlid News, 3 (1), 12–15.

DEMASON, L. (1994b): What's new. Cichlid News, 3 (1), 27.

DERIJST, E. & J. SNOEKS (1992): *Maravichromis* ECCLES and TREWAVAS, 1989, a junior synonym of *Mylochromis* REGAN, 1920 (Teleostei, Cichlidae). Cybium 16 (2), 173.

ECCLES, D.H. (1989a): VI. 4. *Tyrannochromis nigriventer* ECCLES sp. nov. In: ECCLES, D.H. & E. TREWAVAS: Malawian cichlid fishes. The classification of some Haplochromine genera. Lake Fish Movies, Herten, 101–103.

ECCLES, D.H. (1989b): XI. *Aulonocara* REGAN. In: ECCLES, D.H. & E. TREWAVAS: Malawian cichlid fishes. The classification of some Haplochromine genera. Lake Fish Movies, Herten, 138–150.

ECCLES, D.H. & D.S.C. LEWIS (1981): Midwater spawning in *Haplochromis chrysonotus* (BOULENGER) (Teleostei: Cichlidae) in Lake Malawi. Env. Biol. Fish. 6 (2), 201–202.

ECCLES, D.H. & E. TREWAVAS (1989): Malawian cichlid fishes. The classification of some Haplochromine genera. Lake Fish Movies, Herten, 334 pp.

FRYER, G. (1956a): New species of cichlid fishes from Lake Nyasa. Rev. Zool. Bot. Afr. 53, 81–91.

FRYER, G. (1956b): Biological notes on some cichlid fishes from Lake Nyasa. Rev. Zool. Bot. Afr. 54, 1–7.

FRYER, G. (1956c): New species of *Labeotropheus* from Lake Nyasa, with a redescription of *Labeotropheus fuelleborni* AHL and some notes on the genus *Labeotropheus* (Pisces: Cichlidae). Rev. Zool. Bot. Afr. 54, 280–289.

FRYER, G. (1957): A new species of *Gephyrochromis* (Pisces: Cichlidae) from Lake Nyasa, with notes on its ecology and affinities. Revue Zool. Bot. afr. 55, 347–352.

FRYER, G. (1959): The trophic interrelationship and ecology of some litoral communities of Lake Nyasa with special reference to the fishes, and a discussion of the evolution of a group of rock-frequenting Cichlidae. Proc. zool. Soc. Lond. 132, 153–281.

FRYER, G. & T.D. ILES (1972): The cichlid fishes of the great lakes of Africa. Their biology and evolution. Oliver & Boyd, Edinburgh, 641 pp.

GERHARDT, B. & A. SPREINAT (1989): Zwei Arten, ein Name: *Pseudotropheus* „Kingsizei". DCG-Info 20 (8), 151–160.

GREENWOOD, P.H. (1979): Towards a phyletic classification of the „genus" *Haplochromis* (Pisces, Cichlidae) and related taxa. Part I. Bull. Br. Mus. nat. Hist. (Zool.) 33, 297–323.

GREENWOOD, P.H. (1980): Towards a phyletic classification of the „genus" *Haplochromis* (Pisces, Cichlidae) and related taxa. Part II; the species from Lakes Victoria, Nabugabo, Edward, George and Kivu. Bull. Br. Mus. nat. Hist. (Zool.) 39, 1–101.

GÜNTHER, A. (1864): Report on a collection of reptiles and fishes made by Dr. KIRK in the Zambesi and Nyassa regions. Proc. zool. Soc. Lond. 1864, 303–314.

GÜNTHER, A. (1893): Second report on the reptiles, batrachians and fishes transmitted by Mr. H. H. JOHNSTON, C.B., from British Central Africa. Proc. zool. Soc. Lond. 1893, 616–628.

HOLZBERG, S. (1978): A field and laboratory study of the behaviour and ecology of *Pseudotropheus zebra* (BOULENGER), an endemic cichlid of Lake Malawi (Pisces: Cichlidae). Z. zool. Syst. Evolut.-forsch. 16, 171–187.

ILES, T.D. (1960): A group of zooplankton feeders of the genus *Haplochromis* (Cichlidae) in Lake Nyasa. Ann. Mag. nat. Hist. 2 (13), 257–280.

JOHNSON, D.S. (1974): Three new cichlids from Lake Malawi. Today's Aquarist, 1 (3), 38–42.

JOHNSON, D.S. (1975): More new Malawi cichlids. Today's Aquarist 2 (1), 15–18, 20–26.

KNABE, P. (1992): *Labidochromis* sp. „Hongi". In: Das Cichlidenjahrbuch, Cichlid Press, St. Leon-Rot, 53.

KONINGS, A. (1989): Malawi cichlids in their natural habitats. Verduyn Cichlids & Lake Fish Movies, Zevenhuizen und Herten, 303 pp.

KONINGS, A. (1992): Konings Buch der Cichliden und aller anderen Fische des Malawisees. Kollnburg, Germany, 495 pp.

KONINGS, A. (1993): Der „Yellow Black Line". Teil 1: Die Gattungszugehörigkeit von Haplochromis melanonotus REGAN. In: Das Cichlidenjahrbuch, Cichlid Press, St. Leon-Rot, 43–44.

KONINGS, A. (1994): *Pseudotropheus demasoni*: ein neuer Mbuna von der tansanischen Küste des Malawisees. Das Cichlidenjahrbuch, Cichlid Press, St. Leon-Rot, 24–27.

KORTHAUS, E. (1982): Auf Tauchstation im nördlichen Teil des Malawisees. Das Aquarium 155, 226–233.

LEPEL, T. (1993a): Cichliden von der tansanischen Küste des Malawisees. DATZ 46 (8), 513–515.

LEPEL, T. (1993b): Nur eine Art, aber für unsere Aquarien eine doppelte Bereicherung. DCG-Info 24 (10), 218–222.

LEPEL, T. (1994): Ein Schatz aus dem Malawisee. In: Das Cichlidenjahrbuch, Cichlid Press, St. Leon-Rot, 34–35.

Lewis, D.S.C. (1982): A revision of the genus *Labidochromis* (Teleostei: Cichlidae) from Lake Malawi. Zool. J. Linn. Soc. 75, 189–265.

Lewis, D. & P. Reinthal, J. Trendall (1986): A guide to the fishes of Lake Malawi National Park. World Wildlife Found, Gland.

Marsh, A.C. (1983): A taxonomic study of the fish genus *Petrotilapia* (Pisces: Cichlidae) from Lake Malawi. Ichthyol. Bull. Rhodes Univ. 48, 1–14.

Marsh, A.C. & A.J. Ribbink, B.A. Marsh (1981): Sibling species complexes in sympatric populations of *Petrotilapia* Trewavas (Cichlidae, Lake Malawi). Zool. J. Linn. Soc. 71, 253–264.

McKaye, K.R. & T. Kocher (1983): Head ramming behaviour by three paedophagous cichlids in Lake Malawi, Africa. Anim. Behav. 31, 206–210.

Meyer, A. & T.D. Kocher, P. Basasibwaki, A.C. Wilson (1990): Monophyletic origin of Lake Victoria cichlid fishes suggested by mitochondrial DNA sequences. Nature 347, 550–553.

Meyer, M.K. & R. Riehl, H. Zetzsche (1987): A revision of the cichlid fishes of the genus *Aulonocara* Regan, 1922 from Lake Malawi, with descriptions of six new species. In: W. Klausewitz (Ed.): Contributions to the knowledge of the cichlid fishes of the genus *Aulonocara* of Lake Malawi (East Africa). Cour. Forsch.-Inst. Senckenberg 94, 7–53. Senckenbergische Naturforschende Ges., Frankfurt a.M., Germany.

Oliver, M.K. (1975): *Labidochromis textilis*, a new cichlid fish (Teleostei: Cichlidae) from Lake Malawi. Proc. Biol. Soc. Wash. 88 (29), 319–330.

Oliver, M.K. (1989): Systematics of African cichlid fishes: Determination of the most primitive taxon, and studies of the haplochromines of Lake Malawi (Teleostei: Cichlidae).

Unveröffentlicht 1984; Zusammenfassung der Artbeschreibungen in: Eccles, D.H. & E. Trewavas: Malawian cichlid fishes. The classification of some Haplochromine genera. Lake Fish Movies, Herten.

Regan, C.T. (1920): The classification of fishes of the family Cichlidae. 1. The Tanganyika Genera. Ann. Mag. nat. Hist. 5 (9), 33–53.

Regan, C.T. (1922): The cichlid fishes of Lake Nyasa. Proc. zool. Soc. Lond. (1921), 675–727.

Ribbink, A.J. & B.A. Marsh, A.C. Marsh, A.C. Ribbink, B.J. Sharp (1983): A preliminary survey of the cichlid fishes of rocky habitats in Lake Malawi. S. Afr. J. Zool. 18 (3), 149–310.

Ribbink, A.J. & D.S.C. Lewis (1982): *Melanochromis crabro* sp. nov., a cichlid fish from Lake Malawi which feeds on ectoparasites and catfish eggs. Neth. J. Zool. 32, 72–87.

Russ, U. (1993): Neu importiert: *Aulonocara* „Mamelela". DATZ 46 (1), 8.

Seegers, L. (1991): Endlich! Neue *Labidochromis*-Arten aus Tansania. Aquarium Heute 9 (1), 6–8.

Seegers, L. (1992): Ein neuer Mbuna aus Tansania: *Pseudotropheus* spec. „Mbamba Bay, kompakt". Aquarium Heute 10 (4), 174–178.

Spreinat, A. (1985): Selten importierte Cichliden von der Ostküste des Malawisees. DCG-Info 16 (12), 231–239.

Spreinat, A. (1988a): „Fire Crest Mloto". Schwarze Schönheiten aus der Tiefe. Aquarien Magazin 1988 (2), 22–26.

Spreinat, A. (1988b): Robust und schön: Mbunas im Aquarium. DATZ 41 (5), 76–78.

Spreinat, A. (1988c): Die Gattung *Labidochromis* – Zwergcichliden des Malawisees. DATZ 41 (10, 11), 396–400 u. 462–464.

Spreinat, A. (1989a): Wulstlippenbuntbarsche aus dem Malawisee. DATZ 42 (2), 85–90.

Spreinat, A. (1989b): „*Haplochromis*" spec. „hertae" und der falsche „*Haplochromis*" *flavimanus*. Das Aquarium 23 (240), 333–337.

SPREINAT, A. (1989c): Kaiserbuntbarsche des Malawisees. Ulmer, Stuttgart, 106 pp.

SPREINAT, A. (1991): *Petrotilapia*: Dicklippenbuntbarsche aus dem Malawisee. DATZ 44 (2, 3), 82–86, 147–152.

SPREINAT, A. (1992a): Anmerkungen zu einigen *Aulonocara*-Arten. DATZ 45 (9), 573–577.

SPREINAT, A. (1992b): *Lichnochromis acuticeps*. Zur biologischen Funktion seiner ungewöhnlichen Kopfform und der Wulstlippen anderer Cichliden. In: Buntbarsch Jahrbuch 1993, Bede, Ruhmannsfelden, 28–33.

SPREINAT, A. (1993a): Malawisee-Cichliden aus Tansania. DATZ 46 (8), 508–512.

SPREINAT, A. (1993b): *Pseudotropheus callainos*. Anmerkungen zu Verbreitung und ähnlichen Arten. DATZ 46 (9), 578–585.

SPREINAT, A. (1993c): *Stigmatochromis* cf. *pholidophorus*. Freilandbeobachtungen, Pflege und Zucht. In: Buntbarsch Jahrbuch 1994, Bede, Ruhmannsfelden, 25–29.

SPREINAT, A. (1994): Zur Identität von *Pseudotropheus heteropictus* STAECK, 1980. DATZ 47 (2), 107–111.

STAECK, W. (1972): Variabler *Pseudotropheus zebra*. Das Aquarium 6 (41); 1051–1054.

STAECK, W. (1974): Cichliden: Verbreitung, Verhalten, Arten. Pfriem, Wuppertal, 317 pp.

STAECK, W. (1976): Ergebnisse einer ichthyologischen Sammelreise zum Nordende des Nyassasees. Das Aquarium 10 (10, 11), 436–442, 486–492.

STAECK, W. (1977): Cichliden: Verbreitung, Verhalten, Arten. Bd II. Pfriem, Wuppertal, 296 pp.

STAECK, W. (1978): Raritäten aus dem Malawisee. Neuere Erkenntnisse über die Vielgestaltigkeit bei Mbuna-Cichliden. Aquarien Magazin 12 (3), 136–142.

STAECK, W. (1980): *Pseudotropheus heteropictus* n. sp. aus dem Malawisee (Pisces: Cichlidae). Senckenbergiana biol. 60 (3/4), 159–162 (1979).

STAECK, W. (1983): Cichliden III: Entdeckungen und Neuimporte. Pfriem, Wuppertal, 351 pp.

STAECK, W. (1988): Cichliden: Malawisee. Pfriem, Wuppertal, 147 pp.

STAUFFER, J.R. (1988): Three new rock-dwelling cichlids (Teleostei: Cichlidae) from Lake Malawi, Africa. Copeia 3, 663–668.

STAUFFER, J.R. & E. Hert (1992): *Pseudotropheus callainos*, a new species of mbuna (Cichlidae), with analysis of changes associated with two intra-lacustrine transplantations in Lake Malawi, Africa. Ichthyol. Explor. Freshwaters 3 (3), 253–264.

STOLZ, H. (1972): Mbuna. TI, 6 (20) u. 7 (21), 4–6 u. 11–13.

TREWAVAS, E. (1931): Revision of the cichlid fishes of the genus *Lethrinops* REGAN. Ann. Mag. nat. Hist. (10) 7, 133–152.

TREWAVAS, E. (1935): A synopsis of the cichlid fishes of Lake Nyasa. Ann. Mag. nat. Hist. 10 (16), 65–118.

TREWAVAS, E. (1946): The types of African cichlid fishes described by BORODIN in 1931 and 1936, and of two species described by BOULENGER in 1901. Proc. Zool. Soc. Lond. 116 (2), 240–246.

TREWAVAS, E. (1983): Nouvel examen des genres et sous-genres du complexe *Pseudotropheus-Melanochromis* du lac Malawi (Pisces, Perciformes, Cichlidae). Revue fr. Aquariol. 10, 97–106.

TREWAVAS, E. (1984): Un nom et une description pour l'Aulonocara „Sulphur-head", Poisson Cichlide du Lac Malawi. Revue fr. Aquariol. 11, 7–10.

TREWAVAS, E. (1991): Die Gattung *Tyrannochromis* ECCLES & TREWAVAS, 1989. In: Das Cichlidenjahrbuch, Cichlid Press, St. Leon-Rot, 36–39.

ZIERZ, C. (1973): Was man so hört… DCG-Info 3 (11), 124–130.

# Index

Index of cichlids which are comprehensively described in the text and/or are illustrated (bold-faced page numbers refer to illustrations).

Notes

Notes

Notes

Notes